FOREWORD

The Programme centres on road and road transport research, while taking into account the impacts of intermodal aspects on the road transport system as a whole. It is geared towards a technico-economic approach to solving key road transport issues identified by Member countries. The Programme has two main fields of activity:

-- the international co-operation in road and road transport research to provide scientific support for decisions by Member governments and international governmental organisations, and to assess future strategies concerning roads and road transport problems and the priority policy concerns of Member countries;

-- the information and documentation programme (IRRD - International Road Research Documentation), a co-operative scheme that provides a mechanism for the systematic world-wide exchange of information on scientific literature and current research programmes.

The scientific and technical activities concern:

-- the assessment of urban and inter-urban road transport strategies;

-- the development and management of road traffic control and driver communication systems to enhance network efficiency and quality of service;

-- the formulation and evaluation of integrated road and traffic safety programmes;

-- the construction, preservation and rehabilitation of road infrastructure.

ABSTRACT

IRRD No. 294368

The report was prepared by a Scientific Expert Group, created in the framework of the OECD's Road Transport Research Programme. The aim was to review and assess dynamic traffic management systems and strategies likely to improve traffic flow and driving conditions on major arterials of urban and suburban road networks. A special focus is placed on the potential of advanced technologies including in-vehicle communication devices and/or road infrastructure equipment. The Group's report is in six chapters. The introduction presents the background, scope and aims of the study. Chapter II contains an analysis of the objectives of dynamic traffic management. Chapter III provides a functional and technical description of the various dynamic traffic management systems including driver information services, direct traffic control systems and public transport and fleet management systems. Chapter IV discusses human factors, levels of equipment fit, and organisational and legal problems in relation to public acceptance issues. Based on anticipated trends of traffic demand and the most recent developments in advanced technologies, Chapter V identifies and evaluates future strategies and applications of sophisticated traffic management schemes. Finally the Group puts forward conclusions and recommendations for the attention of decision makers, and traffic management authorities at local, regional and national levels as well as research needs directed at the scientific community as a whole.

Subject classification: 73, 91

Fields: Traffic control;
          Vehicle Design and Safety

Keywords: Program (computer), Traffic control, Urban area, Suburbs, Technology, Vehicle, Driver information, Public transport, Human factor, Traffic sign, Variability, Electronics, Tidal traffic, Location, Area traffic control, Real time, Priority (traffic), Traffic signal, Data acquisition, VDU, Traffic, Road network, Driver, Planning specifications, Forecast

EXECUTIVE SUMMARY

BACKGROUND

Car-ownership, road traffic demand and travel needs are increasing worldwide. Recurrent traffic congestion is a well known phenomenon in urban and suburban areas, especially in industrialised countries but also in many metropolitan areas of the Third World. This, together with the constraints on building new road infrastructure in urban areas, has underscored the need for continued R & D on traffic management and control schemes.

Traffic control systems research is now over half a century old, but it is only during the past twenty years that sophisticated and complex control algorithms have been developed and used in practical applications. Dynamic traffic management systems are under development in most industrialised countries. These concern centralised urban traffic control, traffic-responsive ramp metering and dynamic speed control in motorway systems, traffic re-routing using variable message signs, etc. Also, research on advanced driver communication systems and automatic route guidance is underway and this will be summarised in a further OECD study.

STUDY APPROACH

Ten countries participated in the work of this Scientific Expert Group established in the framework of OECD's Road Transport Research Programme. The Group held three plenary meetings at which it looked at the overall problem of dynamic traffic management systems including their classification and objectives as well as their application. The technical and scientific information for drafting the different chapters of this report was provided through national reports submitted by the experts and reviews of research studies and evaluations of traffic systems operated in some Member countries.

The Group's terms of reference approved by the OECD Steering Committee for Road Transport Research, set forth the tasks of the study. Briefly summarised, these included: the analysis of research and experiments carried out in the field of dynamic traffic control systems; user needs and future trends in traffic demand; information and communication issues including data collection and data processing; related human and technical constraints as well as impacts on system elements.

In line with this mandate, the Group focused its work on roads and highway networks, both in urban and suburban areas, keeping in mind that many systems which are described in the report can be used on various types of infrastructure.

Definition and short-term focus

An extensive discussion took place among Members of the Group about what should exactly be considered as "dynamic" traffic management systems. No precise boundary can be defined between real-time traffic responsive systems (reacting in a few seconds) and, for example, traffic actuated or even time-of-day selected traffic signal settings in a predetermined library since both techniques have some degree of "dynamicness". Therefore, the Group considered every system which, in one way or another, depends on traffic changes to be "dynamic".

From the outset, the Group agreed that in practice, emphasis should be laid on those techniques that ensure a better use of the available capacity (space, infrastructure). What still can be done on existing urban networks and facilities is to alleviate the imbalances in the use of available capacities through intelligent re-routing strategies.

Objectives and benefits

In general terms, dynamic traffic management systems should be designed to respond to actual travel needs as generated by economic and social activities, including the improvement of mobility of people, goods and services, subject to societal and resource constraints. Secondary needs are mainly associated with those of traffic management authorities.

Potential system benefits are directly related to better and more efficient management of traffic flows and primarily concern individuals, i.e. more specifically, road users. Factors such as travel time savings, safety, reduction in noise and air pollution and driving comfort are of economic value for the community and provide individuals with additional benefits.

Description of systems

The range of dynamic traffic management systems and facilities as reported to the Group fall into three distinct categories depending on whether they act mainly on "demand", "supply", or both:

-- Driver information systems, by which information is given to the driver who can decide his actions by himself;

-- Direct traffic control systems, by which the driver is influenced directly either through physical means, mandatory instruction, or advisory information;

-- Public transport and fleet control systems.

For each category of systems, the report considers firstly the control strategy employed and secondly the effects in terms of data requirements, gathering, processing and dissemination.

Strategies and data requirements

Driver information services. The strategies employed aim at providing drivers with useful information otherwise not easily or directly available, concerning for instance, longer term incidents or traffic forecasts. The type of information such services may provide includes status messages about incidents, accidents, weather conditions and delays, and advisory messages on route guidance, trip planning information or recommended speeds. Data collection and dissemination are variable from country to country and even between regions in one country. The up-dating of information is a major requirement and essential for drivers' trust in the system and/or compliance.

Direct traffic control. Such systems employ one of two control strategies: they either influence traffic by setting mandatory impedances at key positions in the network, or by providing drivers with information which describes a preferred course of action at a particular site. As regards data requirements, all direct traffic control systems need to collect (measured) information on traffic flows and speeds and all can operate in real time. In practice, these systems have to be treated as self-contained sub-systems within a larger traffic management organisation.

Public transport and fleet management systems. These systems are not directed at traffic in general, but rather at improving the efficiency of operating a particular fleet of vehicles. They employ one of two strategies, i.e. they control traffic signals so that special vehicles can be given priority or they enable a controller to communicate with individual vehicles in the fleet in order to provide a demand responsive service. Data requirements include the need to know the "customer demand" for the service they provide and the status of each vehicle, i.e. occupancy, schedule deviation, alarm status, etc. Information on network conditions may also be required.

Human factors

The successful implementation of dynamic traffic systems depends on whether the individual driver can cope with the tasks imposed on him by such new systems and technologies. Special attention should be given to ergonomic factors related to the driving task (perception of information, problems connected with variable message signs, in-vehicle and aural and/or visual information). Attractiveness and proven reliability will help in enhancing driver acceptance. As regards technical and organisational issues, careful consideration should be given to data gathering aspects and to the management of transmitting centres keeping in mind the requirements and operational capabilities of various parties and agencies involved as well as the legal and regulatory measures required to ensure the credibility of the messages to the driver.

Technology and future directions

The underlying technologies upon which process control systems depend are developing rapidly, and this is true for traffic control systems in particular. Computers (processors) and communications are the dominant technologies, but developments in sensor (detector) and display technologies, as well as control theory, are equally important and are key elements of future traffic management and control systems.

Processing. Mini- and micro-computers will open up an enormous scope for the development of sophisticated and reliable programs which could carry out a number of tasks such as real time simulation and optimisation of large traffic systems.

Communications. Most of the systems available today are based on mature technology (transmission of voice, data and video information). Some future developments such as digital data dissemination, satellite communications, point to multipoint radio data and cellular systems have potential applications to traffic management in a number of different areas.

Sensors. In the short term, some improvements are expected in ultrasonic and radar detectors as well as for the new self-powered vehicle detector. Also, considerable developments and applications of "area-wide" traffic detectors, using image processing techniques are likely.

Displays. Apart from variable message signs which, in spite of some legal and regulatory problems, can now be considered to be a critical element in many present day traffic control facilities, present trends point to a rather rapid evolution of in-car electronics, visual displays, head-up display technology (such as used in aircrafts), and aural communication devices using synthetic speech.

Control theory and techniques. The development of any control system has to meet three fundamental considerations which are observability, controllability and stability and more sophisticated traffic management strategies which will be used in the future should meet these requirements.

A control system is classified according to the level of sophistication of the type of control used. (This is illustrated in Figure V.1 of the final report.) Most traffic control systems today operate at the second level, adjusting signal timing to reflect changing demand. Next is the adaptive control level in which systems automatically alter the parameters of the control mode. Future systems will operate at the fourth level in which the traffic control system will alter the basic form of the control law to respond to changing conditions. This type of control will be particularly important for integrated urban traffic management.

PERSPECTIVES AND RESEARCH NEEDS

The review of new technologies shows that there is tremendous potential for the development of a new generation of dynamic traffic management systems and strategies. To achieve maximum efficiency of the traffic system as a whole, operated often independently through individual traffic control systems, it will be necessary to place greater emphasis on the development of integrated traffic management strategies. This also underscores the need for effective evaluation tools for traffic operations: off-line evaluation in order to define traffic management strategies and on-line evaluation to check changes in traffic patterns which would prompt a modification of the strategy.

Research is required in such areas as:

Driver information systems

-- Standardization of data dissemination protocols;
-- Improvement of traffic data collection;
-- Investigation of ergonomic aspects of in-vehicle information systems;
-- In-depth studies on public acceptance to ensure the proper use of the system.

Direct traffic control

-- Traffic modelling and forecasting methodologies;
-- Development of aids for systems operators;
-- Co-ordination of control strategies;
-- Assessment of new concepts such as image processing, artificial intelligence, automatically driven vehicle, electronic vehicle detection, etc.;
-- Evaluation tools to carefully assess the efficiency of traffic control strategies.

Public transport and fleet control

-- Integration of the various modes including specialised fleets;
-- Forecast studies on the balance between car use and public transport to improve decision-making mechanisms.

*
* *

The report provides policy makers, traffic engineers and scientists with an overall assessment of present progress and research on dynamic control strategies and technology as applied to urban road traffic. International co-operation and research co-ordination are essential to ensure cost/effectiveness of the public and private investments needed for the implementation and use of second generation traffic control and driver communication systems.

TABLE OF CONTENTS

Chapter IV

Chapter VI

Chapter I

INTRODUCTION

I.1. GENERAL

There is an increasing trend toward developing dynamic traffic management systems for the control of traffic lights in towns or on motorway accesses, dynamic driver information systems, as well as monitoring and control systems for buses and special fleets of vehicles.

Up to the recent past, emphasis was put on those techniques which ensure the best possible use of available time, rather than available space (capacity). For a given demand pattern (i.e. a given distribution of travel paths through the network), the problem was to find the best timing of traffic lights to achieve a given objective (minimization of delay, stops, etc.), neither the feed-back effect of this control on demand (route changing behaviour), nor the existence of available spare capacity being directly taken into account. The greatest part of potential benefits attached to this step seems to have been obtained, especially through recent improvements in the dynamicness of systems (adaptive real time systems).

Today, in most large urban and suburban areas of industrialized countries, imbalances in the use of available network capacity are encountered rather frequently. This is due to stochastic variations in traffic demand, incidents, etc. In these cases and for a given set of origin-destination data, some routes are temporarily faster than overcrowded ones, but they are nevertheless not used by drivers due to lack of adequate information and control actions. The result is a time loss both for drivers and the community as a whole.

In such situations, complete traffic management systems integrating not only the classical control over time, but also controls over space (route control) are liable to provide the greatest possible benefits. To do this, the following is necessary:

-- Real-time identification of imbalance situations in the use of available capacity,

-- Definition of adequate strategies, and

-- Implementation of real-time control measures.

Traffic streams can then be directed so as to ensure optimal use of available network capacity, together with controlling traffic signals in order to implement one consistent and comprehensive control strategy. As a matter of fact it should be noted that, the two approaches -- route control and traffic signal control -- can interfere with one another and need to be harmonized.

The development of microelectronics and information technology during the last few years has furthered the use of driver information systems as a means of controlling traffic, especially through the use of in-car electronic equipment providing road-vehicle communications. These new devices allow, in turn, specific improvements in the area of safety and reassurance, parameters which are getting increasing importance in developed countries.

I.2. SCOPE AND AIMS OF THE STUDY

According to the terms of reference, the tasks of the Group were the following:

a) Analysis of research and experiments on this subject, particularly on automatic route guidance and driver communication systems;

b) Evaluation of what is at stake:

. Needs of road users;
. Consideration of future trends in traffic demand;
. Economics.

c) Study of the methods for collecting the necessary information, communicating it to drivers and exploiting it for traffic control purposes;

d) Reflections on the application of such operations and on the constraints that affect them;

. Ability of the driver to perceive the message and to react accordingly (type of distribution of information); acceptance of the system by road users, (psychological),
. Selective communication of the information to the drivers concerned,
. Necessity of creating integrated traffic control systems, considering the compatibility of individual system elements and some standardization of marketed equipment,
. Size of market, who will buy,
. Overall cost and rate of return of the system.

e) Reflections on the strategies to be used in these operations.

Concerning the scope of the study, an extensive discussion took place among Members of the Group about what should exactly be considered as "dynamic" traffic management systems. As a matter of fact, no precise boundary can be defined between real-time traffic responsive systems (reacting in a few seconds) and, for example, traffic actuated or even time-of-day selected traffic signal settings in a predetermined library, both techniques having some degree of "dynamicness". In the following, therefore, the Group considered every system which, in one way or another, depends on traffic changes to be "dynamic".

The Group also decided to focus its work on road and motorway networks, both in urban and suburban areas, leaving aside intercity rural facilities. However, some dynamic traffic management techniques are used in rural areas for instance in France and Germany and these could find some application in urban and suburban areas. Moreover, many systems which are described in this report can be used on all types of infrastructures.

Dynamic control systems for public transport and fleets of specialised vehicles, together with priority systems for emergency vehicles, are considered in this study as part of the urban and suburban traffic system. Many of these systems make use of electronic road-vehicle information devices which could, in some cases, be a forerunner to future individual vehicle information and route guidance systems.

I.3. OUTLINE OF THE REPORT

Chapter II contains an analysis of the objectives of dynamic traffic management, i.e. needs of drivers and traffic management authorities, as well as potential social and economic benefits.

Chapter III gives a functional and technical description of current and planned dynamic traffic management systems. It distinguishes among information systems for drivers, systems giving direct driving indications, and public transport and specialised fleet systems. Each of these three categories of systems is discussed according to the strategies used and the different elements of the information chain: data collection, data processing and data dissemination.

Chapter IV discusses problems regarding human system factors: assimilation of information (both physiological and psychological), levels of equipment fit and driver responses to the indications supplied, as well as organisational and legal problems.

Chapter V presents a prospective view, based on anticipated trends of traffic demand and on the most recent developments in the field of high technology, of what could be the tools and strategies of traffic management at the beginning of the next century.

Finally, Chapter VI presents the Group's conclusions and recommendations in each of the above three categories.

Chapter II

OBJECTIVES OF DYNAMIC TRAFFIC MANAGEMENT SYSTEMS

The general objective of dynamic traffic management systems is to give the most satisfactory answer to travel needs generated by the economic and social activity of individuals and groups. This can be formulated as follows: optimising the mobility conditions supplied to people, goods and services, subject to the constraints of resources: capital, fiscal, energy, environmental impacts, safety and other societal concerns.

In order to satisfy these primary needs, secondary needs which concern people in charge of traffic appear: general organisation of the traffic management system, choice of relevant control tools and strategies, maintenance, etc. (1).

The potential benefits attached to the management of traffic flow are primarily directed at individuals: travel-time savings, safety, cost reduction, decreased pollution, comfort. These factors have nevertheless an economic value for the community as a whole, which can in turn be of additional benefit to the individual (lower fiscal taxes due to community savings, for example).

The different systems which are considered in this report have been classified in three major groups:

-- Driver information systems, by which information is given to the driver who can decide his behaviour by himself;

-- Direct traffic control systems, by which behaviour is indicated to the driver, whether in mandatory or advisory terms;

-- Public transport and fleet control systems.

The few considerations which have been made above give the outline of the chapter: after having pointed out the needs of drivers, the subsequent needs of traffic management authorities are described, followed by insight into potential benefits which could be derived from the extensive use of dynamic traffic management systems.

II.1. NEEDS OF DRIVERS

Drivers wish, of course, to make their travels in the best conditions of time, safety, economy and comfort, and they generally rely on the traffic management authorities to realise these conditions, because they understand that this is a matter of global organisation which, to a large extent, falls out of their control. However, they wish to be given the possibility of implementing individual strategies or at least of knowing the traffic context. Thus, one important need of drivers is information.

As a matter of fact, the general conclusion of the numerous surveys which have been conducted among drivers in different countries (2,3,4,5,6) is that the majority of them wish to get up-to-date information enabling them to manage their trips, either in preparation before the start, or, during travel, by changing their route or simply getting forecasted elements concerning the rest of the trip (intercity travels).

The final report of EUCO-COST 30 [(European Co-operation) Working Group on Road Vehicle Communication] (7), states that the expressed needs of drivers concerning traffic information on major roads are the following:

-- State of the roads (road works, weather conditions);

-- General state of traffic (for travel time estimations);

-- Congestion along the route.

Studies have shown that there are differences between drivers and for the same driver, depending on various situations. As a matter of fact, drivers try to optimise their travel and are interested in any up-to-date information which enables them to make strategic (trip preparation) or tactical (en route) choices. The latter is less frequent, since most drivers, once their route is defined, usually try to stick to it.

Particular situations may influence the nature of the driver's needs as well. For example, when a driver is faced with an unfamiliar situation (unknown route, holiday migration, accident, etc.) he may need more information and be more likely to modify his decisions (departure time, route, etc.) than in familiar situations for which he has already defined his strategy based on personal experience. This behaviour is specific to a certain kind of driver. Others, on the contrary, have a different psychological profile and will hesitate to change their route and take unknown roads.

Because of the wide range of situations and driver profiles, general statements applying to anyone on any occasion are difficult to make. However, generally speaking, the majority of road users wish to decide by themselves and to be made aware of the various events likely to interfere with their plans so as to have the option of changing their route in time whether they would do so or not (for example, in the case of a severe accident on a motorway, being given the information upstream as to the last interchange where the opportunity of leaving the motorway exists). In the same way, drivers wish to make their own decision about the importance of an incident and the suitable behaviour: they prefer factual information to behavioural advice, unless the latter is accompanied with the relevant information. Game theory behaviour can also be observed, when some drivers anticipate the behaviour of others to define their own choice (for example, anticipating the positive effect of official warnings against certain departure times during holiday migrations by starting out at the worst indicated time).

One should notice that driver information, even if it does not give way to route changes, may have positive effects since it increases reassurance and comfort.

Finally, three important features should characterise good road information: up-to-date, valid and relevant. A regular delivery over time and space to accompany the driver along his route is also desirable.

The preceding statements mainly concern intercity motorway (or main road) travel, principally from a route planning point of view.

-- With reference to urban and suburban systems, where travels are generally shorter and primarily daily home-to-work trips, it is likely that driver information needs are fairly similar (specific surveys are lacking in this field), though probably mostly related to incident situations where the question of a route change arises. As a matter of fact, in most traffic-congested situations, on average most drivers, having tested several trip solutions in the past, make good travel choices (route, departure time) according to their work schedule and do not need more information. However, additional information needs may appear (parking availability, for example), which can be met by specific dynamic information systems (parking guidance systems).

-- Regarding information needs related to safety (local information along the chosen route), drivers seem especially interested in systems like ice-warning, fog-warning or queue-warning systems, mainly on motorways where the danger of multi-car accidents is particularly high. In-vehicle driving aids systems, which are intended to enhance the safety conditions of driving (alarm in case of a drop in driver attention, radar and computer vision, enhanced rear vision, etc.) are also being investigated by car manufacturers, but give rise to some ergonomic and behavioural problems. Since they are not under the direct responsibility of Management Authorities, they do not fall within the scope of this work, though Public Authroities will certainly have to regulate their characteristics and use.

A final point is worth mentioning: surveys concerning needs which are presently more or less met by existing information systems (variable signs and media), are quite reliable because responses are based on drivers' experiences. This is not true with surveys where people are asked about planned systems like automatic vehicle location, vehicle-borne route guidance aids or automatic route guidance, because people tend to expect too much from these new systems and have no experience with them. These surveys therefore have to be interpreted with care. However, the well-known drawing effect attached to the introduction of new technologies (new possibilities inducing new needs) must not be discounted and is likely to contribute to their dissemination among drivers, even though, initially their price will probably restrict their use to public institutions (fire brigades, ambulances, police) or private companies (taxis, travel companies, freight companies).

II.2. NEEDS OF TRAFFIC MANAGEMENT AUTHORITIES

II.2.1. Policy

The needs of traffic management authorities are primarily concerned with the type and implementation of the means for realising the best trade-off between the individual's and the community's interests (8). This equilibrium process is illustrated in Figure II.1 where the interactions between public policy and user preferences are shown. Table II.1 points out the different strategies available to management authorities according to their impact (control of supply or control of demand) and time range. In fact, due to the downturn in new construction in recent years, transportation system management (TSM) has been virtually the only option open to the policy maker to address the problems caused by chronic urban traffic congestion.

User interest and community interest are not always consistent. As a matter of fact, it is possible to prove that to minimise the total time spent in a motorway corridor (community optimum), for example it can be advantageous in some cases, to discourage some drivers from entering the motorway at the beginning of the peak period, and make them use surface streets (by restricting access), in order to delay as long as possible the beginning of congestion on the motorway: the total time saving for the other drivers being greater than the total delay experienced by diverted drivers (9). In this case, community and user interests are in competition. However, in most cases any control action which attempts to establish a time equilibrium between competing routes globally decreases the total time spent in the whole system though it does not in general minimise it.

Many other conflicts between objectives can be cited. Side-effects also exist, which oblige management authorities to consider the entire travel demand, all modes included. It is well known, for example, that the modal shift from individual car to public transport (or to car-pool) which was supposed to decrease private car demand is negated because the car which has been left at home is used by the other members of the household, creating new car travel. It is also well-known that any improvement in traffic flow induces an increase in traffic demand, which tends to greatly reduce the anticipated benefits, not only in travel time savings but also in environmental impacts. Consequently, mastering traffic demand becomes one of the most important objectives of traffic management authorities, especially for maintaining the level of service of new or improved facilities. Problems may also be encountered in the field of safety (an increase in free-flow can induce an increase in the severity of accidents) and where several jurisdictions are involved (organisational problems).

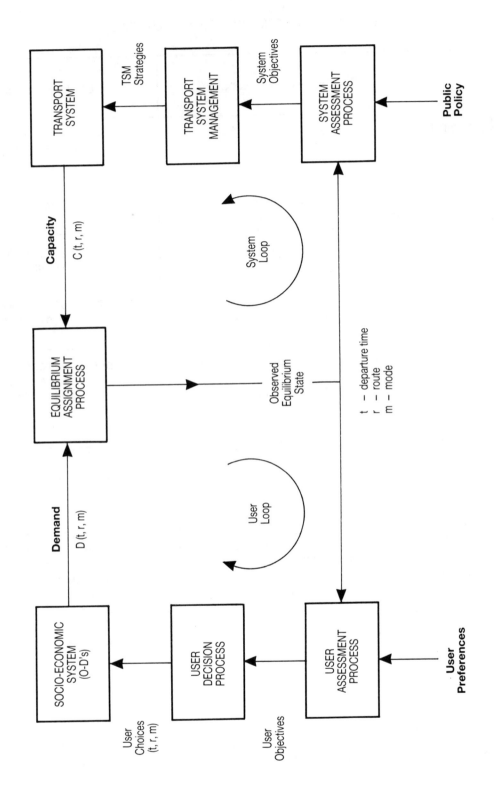

Figure II.1. **TRANSPORT SYSTEM INTERACTIONS**

21

Table II.1

TIME HORIZONS FOR TRAFFIC SYSTEM POLICY IMPACTS

Time span to acheive results		Control of Supply	Control of Demand
	Long Term	Changing structure of transport system (New systems)	Changing spatial distribution of demand (Land use)
	Medium Term	Increase physical capacity of Roadway system (New Construction)	Changing demand volume (Control of private car use and ownership)
	Short term	Improve operational efficiency of existing traffic system (Transportation system management)	Spread demand peaks over time, space and mode

In the following, we will assume, nevertheless, that, provided all these conflicts have been identified and resolved, ensuring an optimal distribution of traffic streams (over time and space) is the general objective of traffic management authorities and entails the best trade-off between individuals and community (travel time, and consequently in most cases, fuel consumption), under the constraint, of course, of a maximum level of safety and a minimum level of environmentally harmful effects (nuisances). This policy is relevant to individual car traffic and normally makes use of driver information and direct traffic control systems. Public transport and fleet management are generally optimised as sub-systems, making use of their own criteria and control systems.

II.2.2. Operation

Dynamic management systems have to cope with operating tasks which define corresponding needs for traffic management authorities. These tasks can be broken down into three steps, which correspond to the three horizontal levels -- data gathering, data processing, data dissemination -- appearing in Figures III.2, III.3 and III.4 in the next Chapter:

-- Detection (or forecast) of critical situations in the road system (urban intersection blocking, motorway saturation due to an incident, etc.). These situations often correspond to a decrease in available capacity and an imbalance of traffic stream distribution. A part of the delay entailed could be eliminated through adequate control actions. At this level, the major problem is the delay of detection of such situations. In places where automatic detection means do not exist, delays of up to 15 minutes or more can occur before the alarm is given. Apart from an extension of automatic systems, improved detection times can be anticipated with future two-way road-vehicle communication equipment.

-- Control strategy elaboration (traffic signal schemes, ramp metering rates, dynamic lane allocation, diversion measures, driver information, etc.). This task may be performed either off-line (predetermined schemes with special user's handbook for implementation) or in real time. There exists a clear need for simulation and operational optimisation tools, which are useful for scientifically defining strategies. Real-time simulation methods are currently being developed as an aid to the operator's decision-making. Growing attention is also paid to the use of knowledge-based systems because in highly saturated conditions, the pragmatic approach which consists of profiting from the experience of the human operator (aided by the computer) appears more feasible than the theoretical approach of maximising a mathematical function.

-- Implementation of adequate actions. This task may be performed either manually, automatically, or computer-aided. Continuous monitoring of the effects of control actions is necessary to detect (or even forecast) the time when it should be cancelled. This avoids traffic instabilities (moving congestion from one location to another) and inconsistent displays of traffic information which greatly reduce traffic management credibility. In this respect, automatic control or automatic monitoring with a warning to the operator, is highly desirable.

A special mention must be made about safety problems, especially those problems which come from hazards (queuing due to accidents, slippery road due to local bad weather conditions, etc.). In view of the great potential benefits and the enormous human stakes attached to the reduction of accident rates, the individual driver should be provided with the relevant warning information. As a matter of fact, some studies clearly show the correlation on motorways between increasing traffic volumes and increasing accident rates. Apart from driving errors which are directly imputable to the driver, one could wonder if the high accident rates noted in many countries are not the consequence of the safety equipment not keeping pace with increasing traffic flows.

Concerning the general problem of driver information, traffic management authorities need a common well-defined traffic information language to be well understood by drivers regardless of the information means.

II.2.3. Maintenance and system efficiency monitoring

All the operational tasks mentioned earlier need extensive electronic equipment for collecting, transmitting, processing and disseminating data. One of the major problems that management authorities have to cope with is the maintenance of this equipment (10). Thus, there is a need to develop new traffic sensors which would be more reliable or easier to repair (without having to stop traffic or close lanes) and design more fail-safe computing configurations (for example, function-dedicated micro-computers linked via a local transmission network) allowing degraded operation for information and control equipment. In the same way, automatic failure detection systems need to be developed.

System efficiency must also be monitored because shifts in the traffic pattern may occur which may necessitate changes in the tuning of control. This makes it necessary to have efficient evaluation tools (statistical methods or simulation models).

On a longer-term basis, evaluation tools based on simulation could also fulfill the need of traffic managers to quantify the potential benefits attached to new investments.

II.3. POTENTIAL BENEFITS

Social requirements, as they have been mentioned above, are sometimes tangible and quantifiable (travel time, safety, energy consumption, noise and air pollution) and sometimes intangible and non-quantifiable (physical and psychological comfort). Those which are quantifiable are not directly comparable; one can only compare and sum them indirectly, using monetary assessment except for noise and air pollution. They can also be differently weighted according to the social group considered (public pressure groups will fight against any diversion scheme which would increase traffic through the town because of the nuisances involved: noise, air pollution, vibration, etc., though it could be a community optimum with respect to travel time, for example). In most cases, the control strategy will result from a trade-off between different objectives, taking into account the different concerns involved, rather than from the optimisation of some general criterion, which would not integrate intangibles. However, quantifiable criteria should be assessed because they are a part of the decision process, even though this one includes political matters.

In the field of quantifiable criteria, dynamic traffic management systems can provide substantial economic gains.

Numerous surveys have shown that urban traffic control systems (on both surface street networks and motorways) are efficient in this respect, and there is a continuous effort to improve this efficiency (especially through an increase in their "dynamicness"). However, the largest potential improvements now seem to be concentrated in the management of imbalance situations, mainly incident and road works situations. Studies have shown that, in some locations, the contribution of recurrent congestion and incident congestion to the total delay on urban motorways were comparable. Great benefits can therefore be anticipated from a reduction of detection times and, above all, a diversion of drivers by means of information actions (variable diversion signs, for example) together with the co-ordination of traffic signals along diversion routes. Such strategies, when using conventional variable message signs, are only feasible in places where a preferential trip direction exists (urban corridor, intercity motorways). However, this limitation will disappear when it is possible to address each driver according to his destination (automatic route guidance systems).

New information systems may give important benefits. For example, a study in the United Kingdom (16) showed that an improved traffic information broadcasting service could save around £40 M per year (at present day prices); mainly from reduced delays at major traffic incidents. A second United Kingdom study, on the potential of improved route guidance (11,12) showed that drivers on average incur about 6 per cent of excess journey costs through poor route choice. About 4 per cent (17) might be recovered by an improved system of guidance, and of this it is significant that a substantial proportion was made up by a large number of drivers making a small number of relatively large errors.

Group 1 of the European Co-operation COST 30 bis (13), estimates that a complete European automatic route guidance and hazard warning system in urban and rural areas would realise benefits (savings in time, distance, safety and road maintenance) of approximately 1984 ECU* 2 400 million per year. The breakdown of these benefits is as follows: fuel costs: 14 per cent; other vehicle running costs: 36 per cent; vehicle occupants time: 40 per cent; accidents: 5 per cent; and road maintenance: 5 per cent. Additional benefits are also anticipated, such as reduced anxiety and the possibility of improved traffic control procedures. Half of these benefits (ECU 1 200 million) could be achieved by a historic (non-traffic responsive) route guidance system, which would require a minimum total investment (public and private).

Those benefits have, of course, to be related to infrastructure and in-vehicle equipment costs. A German study (14) has evaluated the costs and benefits of a motorist information and communication system based on in-vehicle equipment together with an extensive communication infrastructure. Public investment was estimated at around $460 million for all of West Germany. The benefits, including travel time savings decreased accidents and fuel consumption, ranged from $540 to $635 million per year according to the different alternatives investigated (car equipment rates of from 20 to 50 per cent, total network of motorways only, infra-red or induction loop infrastructure, one-way or two-cay communication). A study by the United States Federal Highway Administration (15), investigating the feasibility of in-vehicle route guidance systems in the metropolitan area of Rochester (N.Y.), also gives interesting results ($3-12 million savings). Estimating that 15 to 20 per cent of urban area motorists in the United States may be reasonably expected to purchase the equipment (whose price would be around $60), the potential benefits are estimated at around $740 million per year,

---

* ECU = European Currency Unit.

including time and fuel consumption savings, while the infrastructure equipment is estimated at around $260 million (infra-red beacons) or $170 million (microwave beacons).

All these studies, though based on different assumptions, exhibit important potential net benefits which could justify for traffic administrations the development of dynamic driver information and guidance systems.

Of course, only a part of these benefits could be obtained initially. As a matter of fact, considering the problems attached to in-car equipment development (frequency allocation, need for international compatibility, need for very good data collection to justify the price of the equipment by an efficient operation, industrial risks, etc.), the dissemination of these systems, both geographically and among drivers, will be evolutionary. For example, it will first entail vehicle-borne route guidance with electronic mapping (historic, no communication), then updating via radio broadcasts (traffic responsive, one-way communication), then automatic route guidance (two-way communication). Touristic information and advertising could also be used as incentives for the development of such equipment. At-home or at-the-roadside interactive driver information equipment, which is being made feasible thanks to the development of telematics, can also be used as route planning aids, as is already the case in some countries.

REFERENCES

1. COHEN, S. et al. Ingéniérie de la circulation routière: un état de l'art. INRETS. Paris, Feb. 1985.

2. ANDREW, C. An interview survey of motorway driver information requirements and signal understanding. LR 742. TRRL. Crowthorne, 1977.

3. JAPANESE MINISTRY OF CONSTRUCTION. Needs of road information. Traffic engineering laboratory. Japanese Ministry of Construction. Tokyo, 1984.

4. SMITH, SA. and MILLER, LM. Concepts for a low cost motorist information system. FHWA. Washington, 1984.

5. CAUBET, C. Attentes des conducteurs et besoins en information routière. SETRA/DTCS. Paris, June 1984.

6. COTTINET, M et al. Information routière -- bibliographie sur les besoins d'information et les méthodes. Working group report. INRETS. Paris, Feb. 1986.

7.	EUCO-COST 30. Survey of information needs. Theme 5 final report on Electronic Traffic Aids on Major Roads. Commission of the European Community. Brussels, Jan. 1980.

8.	CARRE, JR. Etude des besoins des exploitants de la route en matière de moyens de communication avec les conducteurs. INRETS. Paris, Dec. 1977.

9.	MORIN, JM. Urban motorway corridor control: general principles, ramp metering, ramp assignment. Encyclopedia of systems and control. Pergamon Press Ltd. Oxford, to be published.

10.	CLELAND, A. and KIRK, I. Maintenance aspects of centrally integrated traffic control systems. International conference on road traffic signalling. IEE. London, April 1982.

11.	JEFFERY, D. The potential benefits of route guidance. Report LR 997. TRRL. Crowthorne, 1981.

12.	JEFFREY, D. Ways and means for improving driver route guidance. Report 1016. TRRL. Crowthorne, 1981.

13.	EUCO-COST 30 BIS. Road/vehicle electronic communication. Group 1 final report. Electronic Aids on Major Roads. Commission of the European Community. Brussels, 1984.

14.	BEHRENDT, J. Development of an in-car motorist information and communication system. OECD Seminar on micro-electronics for road and traffic management. Traffic Bureau National Police Agency. Tokyo 1985.

15.	FHWA. Study of the feasibility and design configuration for in-vehicle route guidance. Report RD-81/055. FHWA. Washington, May 1981.

16.	TRRL. Report of the working group on the broadcasting of traffic information. SR506. TRRL. Crowthorne, 1979.

17.	JEFFERY, D. and RUSSAM, K. Information systems for drivers. Transportation planning and technology. Volume 9. TRRL. Crowthorne, 1984.

Chapter III

DESCRIPTION OF DYNAMIC TRAFFIC MANAGEMENT SYSTEMS

Traffic conditions depend upon the ability of a road network (the supply) to meet the traffic flows resulting from the travel requirements of drivers (the demand). Dynamic management systems may act on either, in the ways shown in Figure III.1.

The range of systems which were reported to the Working Group as providing dynamic management facilities is given in Annex 1. They fall into three distinct categories depending on whether they act mainly on "supply", "demand" or both.

Systems which affect "demand" (loop 1 in Figure III.1) are "Driver Information Systems". Their main function is either:

i) to provide drivers with "trip planning" advice: drivers' routes, mode of travel and departure times may be influenced if they can be given advance warning of current and anticipated conditions on the road network; or

ii) to provide drivers with "route following" advice: the actual routes followed by drivers may be influenced to avoid congestion sites as well as to reduce waste caused through inefficient route choice.

Systems which affect "supply" (loop 2 in Figure III.1) are the "Direct Traffic Control Systems". Their main function is either:

iii) to provide "flow control" measures: the numbers and speeds of drivers entering congested areas may be influenced by introducing impedances (e.g. traffic signals or warning signs) at selected points in the network or by giving warnings (e.g. area broadcasts) in selected areas of the network; or

iv) to provide "traffic management information": improved systems for collecting and collating information may reduce both the time and resources needed to deal with traffic incidents and can enable systems to respond automatically to changing traffic conditions.

A further method of affecting both "supply" and "demand" is:

v) through "Public Transport and Fleet Management Systems": public transport, taxi, and emergency service vehicles may be organised and deployed more efficiently by a controller if he can locate and communicate with his drivers while they are on the move, and give them priority at traffic signals: this may in turn affect "demand" through influencing mode choice or "supply" by facilitating the early alleviation of incidents and hazards.

Figure III.1. **DYNAMIC TRAFFIC MANAGEMENT OVERVIEW**

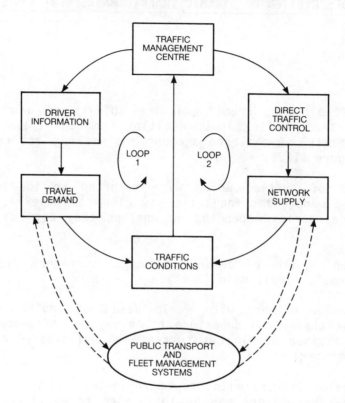

In the following, the functions and operation of each of the different classes of systems which have been identified are first described. Then, a technical description in terms of control strategies and data requirements for the three main categories -- Driver Information, Direct Traffic Control, Public Transport and Fleet Management -- is given.

III.1 CLASSES OF SYSTEMS

The classification of systems shown in Table III.1 was developed from the above discussion. The Table distinguishes 14 classes of Dynamic Traffic Management systems, subdivided into "Driver Information Services", "Direct Traffic Control Systems", and "Public Transport and Fleet Management Systems", and ranks them according to the main function [points (i) through (v) above, shown underlined in Table III.1] which they provide. The ranking broadly reflects the "dynamicness" of the systems and their relative usefulness to drivers and traffic control authorities.

Table III.1

CLASSES OF DYNAMIC TRAFFIC MANAGEMENT SYSTEMS

Class of System	Trip planning	Route following	Flow control	Traffic management information	Fleet control	Status Key: 1. existing 2. experimental 3. planned)
DRIVER INFORMATION SERVICES -- PREPARATION FOR THE TRIP						
1. Media	_X_					1
2. Telephone pre-trip information services	_X_	X				1
3. Teletext pre-trip information services	_X_					1
4. Videotex route planning services	_X_	X				1
DRIVER INFORMATION SERVICES -- WHILE DRIVING						
5. Special traffic information broad-casting services	X	_X_	X			1
6. Citizens Band (CB) radio	X	_X_	X	X		2
7. Vehicle-borne route guidance aids with broadcast updating	X	_X_	X			3
DIRECT TRAFFIC CONTROL SYSTEMS						
8. Variable message signs & route control systems		X	_X_	X		1
9. Historic UTC, Tidal Flow & Ramp Metering systems			_X_	X		1
10. Adaptive UTC, Tidal Flow & Ramp Metering systems			_X_	X		1
11. Automatic route guidance systems		X	_X_	X		3
12. Road pricing and automatic vehicle location systems			_X_	X		2
PUBLIC TRANSPORT AND FLEET MANAGEMENT SYSTEMS						
13. Signal priority systems					_X_	1
14. Vehicle fleet command & control systems					_X_	1

*underlined = main function

31

III.1.1. Driver information services

The systems in this category are essentially services. They fall naturally into one of two sub-divisions depending on whether their primary function is to help the driver prepare for his trip, or to help him while he is on the move (5).

a) Preparation for the Trip

These services provide the driver with information at his home, at his work place, or at selected roadside sites such as rest areas. They essentially fulfill a "trip planning" function.

Class 1: Media

Newspapers and everyday news bulletins broadcast on radio and television are a useful means of disseminating traffic information for trip planning. Information describing major long term or predictable incidents can be given so that drivers may be influenced to avoid major roadworks, or to modify their routes and departure times during peak holiday periods, or when bad weather conditions are forecast. The information provided is usually fairly general since it must cater to all drivers in a region or even an entire country, but it can be expected to reach a wide audience.

Class 2: Telephone Pre-Trip Information Services

Drivers may also obtain trip planning information over the telephone: either by dialing a special number provided by the telephone company, which gives access to pre-recorded messages describing road conditions in a region; or by calling an Automobile Club or similar organisation which can provide travel information. (These organisations are usually only for members). This service is interactive, i.e. it provides answers to specific questions. Questions most commonly asked are about weather and traffic conditions on a particular route, or the best route at a particular time. The service can therefore provide some information of use in "route following".

Class 3: Teletext Pre-trip Information Services

Teletext, i.e. broadcasting of pages of text or simple graphics over a television channel, represents a technological extension of Class 1 (media) and is free to anyone with access to a suitably adapted television receiver. Most television broadcasting companies provide several pages of traffic information on teletext services such as CEEFAX in the United Kingdom. In France, the ANTIOPE service displays regional road maps showing the location and severity of congestion on major roads. The information is useful for "trip planning".

Class 4: Videotex Route Planning Services

Videotex combines the interactive capability of the Class 2 (telephone) services with the television display capabilities of the Class 3 (teletext) services. The driver must make a telephone call to connect him with a central computer. In the French TELETEL system he can then request maps of road conditions at various levels of detail. While using the United Kingdom's experimental ROUTE-TEL system, he can request a set of route instructions which are suited to his vehicle type and individual journey criteria together with warnings of any hazards he can expect to encounter on his journey. A printer is provided so that the driver can take a copy of the route instructions with him. For the future, it is proposed to use Cellular radio so that a driver can have access to the system directly from his vehicle.

Videotex systems therefore provide useful "trip planning" information and have the potential to provide useful "route following" information.

b) Information Systems While Driving

These systems employ special vehicle units to provide information directly to the driver in his vehicle while he is on the move. They mainly fulfill a "route following" function.

Class 5: Special Traffic Information Broadcasting Services

Special broadcasting services, such as ARI in Germany or HAR in the United States, can provide valuable "trip planning" information but their greatest potential is in providing drivers with information in real time about conditions on the roads in the area in which they are driving and to describe alternative routes around congested areas. These systems therefore provide a "route following" function although advice is not vehicle specific and can only be given in general terms which will satisfy the largest number of drivers. In addition, because the area covered by the broadcasts and their repetition rate can be controlled, these systems also have potential to provide a "flow control" function.

Class 6: Citizen's Band Radio

Citizen's Band (CB) radio provides a 2-way communication link between drivers or between drivers and fixed stations and can in principle be used to provide a similar service and fulfill the same functions as a Class 5 (special broadcasting) system. Moreover, the system is interactive: the driver can obtain answers to specific questions and also report on road conditions to other drivers. The CB radio can therefore be used to gather information about conditions on the road network, i.e. to provide a "traffic management information" function. In practice, the CB radio is not widely accepted as a reliable means to convey information and to manage traffic, mainly because its use is unregulated. However, it is extensively used in North America and in Europe and attempts are being made to harness its potential for traffic control [for example, the American MAS (Motorist Aid System)].

Class 7: Vehicle Borne Route Guidance Aids with Radio Broadcast Updating

No examples of these systems exist as yet but research on so-called "autarkic" (i.e. self-contained) route guidance systems is actively being undertaken by numerous motor and electronics manufacturing companies in several countries. These devices rely on an "electronic map" carried in the vehicle and some form of navigation system to enable drivers to keep track of their position in the network. Some systems, e.g. ETAK in the United States, display a map of the surrounding road network with the driver's position superimposed, while others, e.g. EVA in Germany or CARIN in the Netherlands, offer route guidance by deducing the best routes and giving drivers turn instructions as they proceed on their journey. In these systems the "electronic maps" are historic but COST 30 (1) has proposed that the maps could be updated using digital radio broadcasts. The systems would then be useful for "trip planning" as well as "route following" and, if enough vehicles became equipped, for "flow control".

III.1.2. Direct traffic control systems

These systems control traffic by setting variable impedances in the network. They essentially fulfill a "flow control" function, though systems which incorporate an automatic data collection facility, also provide "traffic management information".

Class 8: Variable Message Sign and Route Control Systems

Variable message signs are used at the roadside in most countries to set speed limits and to advise drivers of conditions on the road ahead or to advise them on the best route to follow to reach their destination. Many systems exist in most countries, for example: Glasgow's CITRAC system, Canada's QEW/Burlington Skyway scheme, the Dutch MTCS (Motorway Traffic Control System), the English Motorway Traffic Signalling System and in France the Paris Boulevard Périphérique Information System.

Data collection systems may also be used so that the signs can be automatically varied in real time to take account of changing traffic conditions. These systems therefore provide "route following", "flow control", and "traffic management information", functions. The amount of information that can be given is very limited however, and destinations can only be described in very broad terms. The route control aspect of these systems is therefore generally reserved for known congestion sites, e.g. bridges and tunnels, where a limited number of clearly identifiable alternative routes are available.

A novel form of variable message sign is under investigation in Italy where Teletext is used at entrances to motorway toll points to warn drivers of adverse conditions on the road ahead. New variable message signs (pictograms) have recently been demonstrated on a Dutch motorway in the frame of COST 30 bis (1). Some of them have been recommended to the European Conference of Ministers of Transport (ECMT) for normalization.

Class 9: Historic Urban Traffic Control, Tidal Flow and Ramp Metering Systems

These are all traffic signal control systems. The Urban Traffic Control (UTC) systems control and co-ordinate traffic signals on junction approaches in an attempt to minimise overall delays experienced by crossing flows of traffic in urban networks. Examples include most UTC systems currently in use which employ programs such as TRANSYT to determine signal timing plans.

Tidal Flow systems control special traffic signals over the individual lanes of a carriageway so that the number of lanes assigned to each direction can be varied to accomodate the direction experiencing the greatest demand. An example is to be found on the Albert Bridge in London where all of the three lanes are allocated to inbound traffic in the morning and out-bound traffic during the evening peak periods.

Ramp Metering systems employ traffic signals and sometimes variable message signs at on-ramps to control the rate at which vehicles can enter a motorway.

All these systems are not strictly dynamic traffic control systems. They use fixed time plans based on historic data to control a system of traffic signals. But because the plans may be changed as often as every 15 minutes during the peak hours they exhibit a degree of "dynamicness" and are therefore included for completeness. The historic data must be updated every year or so, so that some "traffic management information" is obtained, but these systems essentially provide only "flow control".

Class 10: Adaptive Urban Traffic Control, Tidal Flow and Ramp Metering Systems

These represent a more recent development in traffic control signalling systems and are truly dynamic in that they collect their own traffic data in order to respond to changing conditions in real time. They therefore provide "flow control" and "traffic management information". Examples include: UTC systems based on SCOOT from the United Kingdom, PRODYN from France and SCATS from Australia; Tidal Flow systems such as those operating within the Sydney SCATS system; and most Ramp Metering systems such as those used on Highway 401 in Canada and in the Northern Long Island Corridor in the United States. "SCOOT" is currently employed or being installed in some 30 cities in the United Kingdom and elsewhere throughout the world, and is being further investigated to show the potential of the traffic data collected for providing information on traffic incidents and trends as well as for providing route guidance advice.

Class 11: Automatic Route Guidance Systems

No examples of these systems exist except as experiments e.g. ALI from Germany and CACS from Japan. However, they have the potential to significantly increase the efficiency of network usage and hence to provide the next generation of traffic control tools. They require an extensive roadside infrastructure and units in vehicles which together enable drivers to receive guidance at junctions to direct them over a minimum path route to their individual destinations. At the same time, data on traffic movements is collected. Equipped vehicles can then be guided in real time and in such a way as to distribute traffic more evenly throughout the network and to alleviate congestion at the sites of incidents. These systems therefore provide "route following", "flow control", and "traffic management information" functions.

In practice, there is potential for overlap between these and the Class 7 systems. In the AUTO-SCOUT system from Germany, for example, an infra-red light beam is used to communicate up-to-date map information from a roadside unit to a vehicle unit which is essentially a Class 7 device. But map information transmitted is only sufficient to enable the vehicle to navigate for itself until the next equipped junction. If the communication link was made 2-way and sufficient junctions were equipped, this system could provide the same facilities and fulfill the same functions as a Class 11 system.

Class 12: Road Pricing and Automatic Vehicle Location Systems

Electronic Road Pricing (ERP) systems also require an extensive roadside infrastructure and vehicle units. An example is the experimental ERP System in Hong Kong in which vehicles are both located and charged as they cross "toll points" distributed in the network. For these systems however, the fitting of vehicle units is mandatory and an exceptionally high integrity road-vehicle communication link is required to ensure that vehicles are not mistakenly identified or wrongly charged. These systems provide "flow control" and "traffic management information" functions.

Automatic Vehicle Location (AVL) systems are normally incorporated into the Vehicle Fleet Command and Control systems of Class 14 which are discussed below. The German AUTONOTFUNK system is an exception: it is designed for use by all traffic. In this system vehicles must be equipped with a special unit which radiates a special frequency when the driver activates an alarm button. The frequency is then monitored by three or more fixed receivers in the network. The direction from which the signals are received at the monitoring stations enables the position of the vehicle to be located. At the same time a voice channel is opened so that the driver and a control centre can communicate with one another.

III.1.3. Public transport and fleet management systems

These systems are increasingly used to improve the operational and economic efficiency of fleets of vehicles. They provide improved deployment, productivity, and scheduling; better working conditions; and energy savings. In the case of public transport or freight operations, they also provide improved levels of customer service, such as reduced waiting times, higher running speeds, more reliable timetables, and in some cases, response on demand (e.g. "dial-a-bus"), or information displays which show when the next vehicle is due (2).

The systems generally operate in real time and are therefore dynamic, but they do not strictly provide a means for general traffic control except in so far as: (i) journey times by public transport may be significantly reduced and a proportion of drivers may be encouraged to forsake their vehicles in favour of public transport -- the general level of congestion on the network may thereby be reduced; or (ii) emergency services may be summoned more quickly to deal with hazards and so help maintain the traffic capacity of the network at a higher level.

Class 13: Signal Priority Systems

These are special systems which enable public transport or emergency service vehicles to receive priority at signalised intersections. They operate in real time by automatically detecting specially equipped vehicles as they approach the traffic signals. Examples of these systems are to be found in major cities in most countries.

Class 14: Vehicle Fleet Command and Control Systems

These systems generally rely on private mobile radio systems to enable a fleet controller to communicate with, and keep track of the position and status of the vehicles in his fleet. In some public transport systems, e.g. London Transport's BUSCO, and Toronto Transit Commission's CIS, an additional infrastructure of roadside beacons or transponders is employed to assist with more accurate vehicle location.

The three key components of all 14 classes of dynamic traffic management systems are: first, data gathering; second, data processing; and third, data dissemination. As a result of the last, it is expected that traffic conditions will be modified and this will in turn affect the data which is subsequently gathered. The control loop, whether on the "supply" or "demand" side of Figure III.1, is thus closed to provide a control system whose output is continually (i.e. dynamically) modified by feedback to control traffic conditions on the network.

In practice, the quality of the control which can be achieved is dependent on a number of factors, including the quality of the information gathered, the time lags in the system, the output (i.e. the means for controlling traffic), and the proportion of drivers who are influenced by the output.

In the three following sections for each category of systems, i.e. "Driver Information Services", "Direct Traffic Control Systems", and "Public Transport and Fleet Management Systems", we consider first the control strategies employed (Table III.2) and, second, the effects on data requirements (Table III.3) in terms of the various aspects of data gathering, processing, and dissemination (Figures III.2, III.3, and III.4).

III.2. DRIVER INFORMATION SERVICES

III.2.1. Traffic control strategies

The Driver Information Services of Classes 1 through 7 attempt to influence traffic by making information available to drivers about conditions

Table III.2

TRAFFIC CONTROL STRATEGIES

Class of System	Driver information services / Direct traffic control — Provide Drivers With Information					Public Transport & Fleet Management Systems	
	Status Messages		Advisory Messages			Mandatory roadside impedances	Fleet control instructions
	Incident types & location	Delays	Route guidance (*)	Trip planning (**)	Recommended speed		
DRIVER INFORMATION SERVICES -- PREPARATION FOR THE TRIP							
1. Media	X	X	a	X	X		
2. Telephone pre-trip information services	X	X	a	X	X		
3. Teletext pre-trip information services	X	X	a	X	X		
4. Videotex route planning services	X	X	b	X	X		
DRIVER INFORMATION SERVICES -- WHILE DRIVING							
5. Special traffic information broadcasting services	X	X	a	X	X		
6. Citizens Band (CB) radio	X	X	a	X	X		
7. Vehicle-borne route guidance aids with broadcast updating	X	X	b	X	X		
DIRECT TRAFFIC CONTROL SYSTEMS							
8. Variable message sign & route control systems	X	X	b		X	X	
9. Historic UTC, Tidal Flow & Ramp Metering systems						X	
10. Adaptive UTC, Tidal Flow & Ramp Metering systems						X	
11. Automatic route guidance systems	X	X	b		X		
12. Road pricing & automatic vehicle location systems						X	
PUBLIC TRANSPORT AND FLEET MANAGEMENT SYSTEMS							
13. Signal priority systems						X	
14. Vehicle fleet command & control systems							X

Notes::   *   a = general advice only; b = at junction route guidance -- see text.
          **   e.g. time of departure, mode choice, parking availability.

in the network and, in some cases, by providing advice on how to avoid congested or hazardous areas, or peak congestion periods. The strategy therefore is, as shown in Table III.2, to "provide drivers with information". In practice, no distinction needs to be made between the "preparation for the trip" and "while driving" systems, except to say that the "trip planning" services must place greater emphasis on longer term incidents and forecasts at the expense of real time information while the opposite is true for the "while-driving" systems.

For these systems Table III.2 shows the types of messages which they can provide; these include: "Status" and "Advisory" messages. "Status messages" describe the conditions prevailing at the site of a traffic incident and include: (i) "incident type and location", i.e. a description of a traffic incident such as roadworks, an accident, bad weather conditions, etc. which give rise to congestion and hazardous conditions, and its location; and (ii) "delays", i.e. an indication of the severity of the congestion which the incident causes.

Advisory messages inform the driver of what action he should take and include: (iii) "route guidance", i.e. advice on if and how to avoid the incident; (iv) "trip planning" information, e.g. advice on, for example, mode choice, parking availability and the best time to set off on a holiday trip during peak holiday periods; and (v) "recommended speed", i.e. advice on any speed limits imposed at the site of an incident.

Route guidance messages are further subdivided in Table III.2 to show two levels of precision. At the higher level "b", guidance is personalised, i.e. is specific to a particular vehicle and is given on the approaches to individual junctions. At the lower level "a", guidance advice can only be given in very general terms which will be useful to the greatest number of drivers regardless of their particular journey.

III.2.2. Data requirements

Table III.3 shows the data that must be gathered in order that the systems can implement the strategies shown in Table III.2. The data requirements are the same for all the Driver Information Systems and include (i) "incident type and location"; (ii) "reduced traffic capacity", i.e. a measure for forecasting the likely impact of the hazard in terms of congestion; and (iii) "delays", i.e. a measure of the severity of the congestion caused by the incident.

The means by which data is gathered, collated and disseminated is extremely variable and differs from country to country, and even between regions in any one country. However Figure III.2 shows a general configuration for these services together with the essential elements of data gathering, processing, and dissemination. Data flows and the types of communication links used for transferring data between the various elements are also indicated.

Table III.3

DATA REQUIREMENTS

Class of System	Incident type & location	Reduced traffic capacity	Delays	Measured speeds, flows	Individual vehicle identification
DRIVER INFORMATION SERVICES					
-- PREPARATION FOR THE TRIP					
1. Media	X	X	X		
2. Telephone pre-trip information services	X	X	X		
3. Teletext pre-trip information services	X	X	X		
4. Videotex route planning services	X	X	X		
DRIVER INFORMATION SERVICES					
-- WHILE DRIVING					
5. Special traffic information broadcasting services	X	X	X		
6. Citizens Band (CB) radio	X	X	X		
7. Vehicle-borne route guidance aids with broadcast updating	X	X	X		
DIRECT TRAFFIC CONTROL SYSTEMS					
8. Variable message sign & route control systems	X	X	X	X	
9. Historic UTC, Tidal Flow & Ramp Metering systems				historic	
10. Adaptive UTC, Tidal Flow & Ramp Metering systems				X	
11. Automatic route guidance systems	X	X		X	
12. Road pricing & automatic vehicle location systems				X	X
PUBLIC TRANSPORT AND FLEET					
MANAGEMENT SYSTEMS					
13. Signal priority systems					X
14. Vehicle fleet command & control systems					X

a) Data Gathering

Sources of Data

Six "primary" sources of data are shown reporting directly to the Traffic Management Centre. These include (i) the police; and (ii) the private (motoring) organisations, both of which may employ air as well as ground patrols to assist them in gathering data about traffic conditions and incidents (e.g. accidents, congestion, public events, vehicle breakdowns, shed loads, emergency weather hazards, signal failures, etc.); (iii) the road construction and maintenance authorities for information on predictable roadworks; (iv) the meteorological offices for information on weather conditions and forecasts; (v) the public utilities for information on predictable and emergency roadworks concerning gas, water, electricity supply and railway crossing repairs, etc.; and (vi) closed circuit television (CCTV) and automatic surveillance, e.g. incident, weather and traffic data collection systems which feed information directly to the traffic management centre.

The primary data sources usually have formal communication procedures with the traffic management centres which may, as shown in the figure, employ Telex, Fax, or Videotex systems operating over private or leased lines. Less formal links may exist with the public utilities, while dedicated, and in some instances, highly specialised links may be used to connect the automatic surveillance systems with the traffic management centre.

A valuable "secondary" source of data is provided by individual motorists and members of the public who may contact the police or the motoring organisations directly with information about traffic incidents. Communication may be via CB radio, the public telephone network, private or leased lines installed for emergency telephones or Motorist Aid Systems (MAS) on motorways and other main roads, or by special systems such as the mobile radio link used in the AUTONOTFUNK emergency alarm system in Germany.

Quality of Data

Information provided by the primary information sources is generally accepted as valid and accurate. However its relevance, in terms of actual traffic consequences, will often need to be directly observed by the police or motoring organisations, as will all data provided from secondary sources.

The quality of the information gathered is then largely governed by the area of the network affected by the incident and the resources which can be deployed to monitor its progress through time. A single observer in a car, for example, will give a very incomplete picture of what is occurring on the ground compared with that which an air patrol or comprehensive CCTV coverage could provide. As a result, the quality of information gathered is often very variable.

b) Data Processing

Operation

In Figure III.2 data processing is carried out in the traffic management centre where all reports of traffic importance are validated, collated and prioritised. The information must then be prepared in a format which is suitable for dissemination using the various means available.

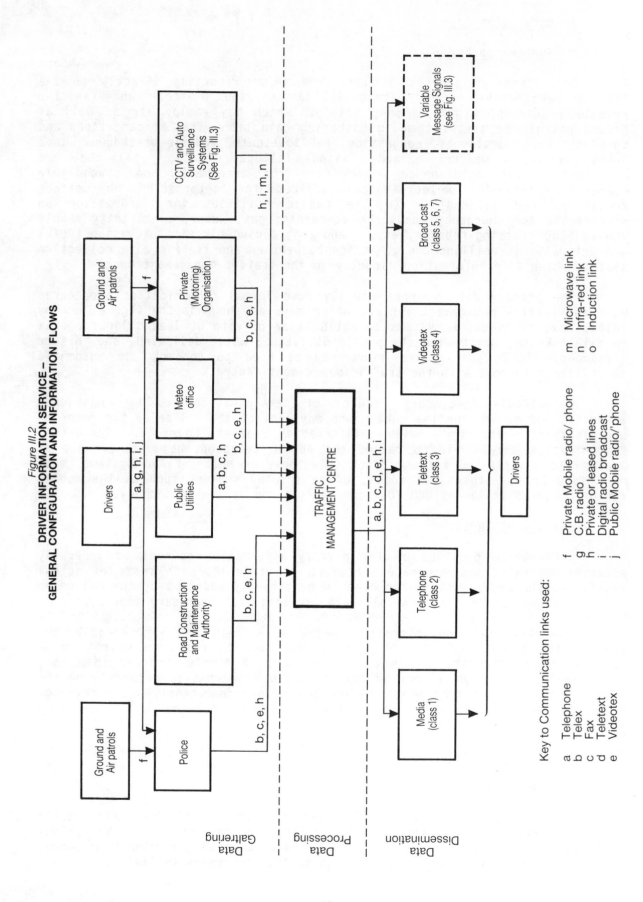

Figure III.2
DRIVER INFORMATION SERVICE –
GENERAL CONFIGURATION AND INFORMATION FLOWS

Data Gathering

Data Processing

Data Dissemination

Ground and Air patrols

Drivers

Ground and Air patrols

CCTV and Auto Surveillance Systems (See Fig. III.3)

Private (Motoring) Organisation

Meteo office

Public Utilities

Road Construction and Maintenance Authority

Police

TRAFFIC MANAGEMENT CENTRE

Variable Message Signals (see Fig. III.3)

Broad cast (class 5, 6, 7)

Videotex (class 4)

Teletext (class 3)

Telephone (class 2)

Media (class 1)

Drivers

a, g, h, i, j

a, b, c, h

b, c, e, h

b, c, e, h

b, c, e, h

b, c, e, h

h, i, m, n

f

f

a, b, c, d, e, h, i

Key to Communication links used:

a   Telephone
b   Telex
c   Fax
d   Teletext
e   Videotex

f   Private Mobile radio/ phone
g   C.B. radio
h   Private or leased lines
i   Digital radio broadcast
j   Public Mobile radio/'phone

m   Microwave link
n   Infra-red link
o   Induction link

42

This is something of an ideal picture, for in practice the traffic management centres tend to be distributed. There are many and diverse sources of data and, depending on the particular class of system, the data may need to be co-ordinated at a local, regional or even national level. Where more than one traffic management centre exists in a country they should therefore communicate in order to collate their reports and operate according to a single and consistent standard of practice.

Frequency of Up-dating

The number of traffic incidents occurring on major roads in Europe is reported by EUCO-COST 30 (3) to range from about 40 per km per year in the open country to around 400 per km per year on busy sections of urban motorways. Some 30-50 per cent are caused by roadworks and are in principle therefore known about in advance -- as also are public events, some abnormal loads (exceptional convoys), and some long term forecasts of bad weather conditions. The remainder are unpredictable and between 25 and 40 per cent last for more than 30 minutes.

For the predictable incidents, warnings can be prepared in advance and the police alerted to monitor any likely problem areas. In these cases, incidents can either be forecast or reported almost as soon as they occur.

Many incidents, however, cannot be predicted. They may be detected very quickly by automatic surveillance systems or more slowly by manual reporting methods. But in the worst cases, the police will usually learn of their existence within about 10 minutes of their occurrence and by the time they have verified the incident, some 20 to 30 minutes may have elapsed before the information has been processed by the traffic control centre.

Dissemination can therefore occur in advance or at worse, within about 30 minutes of an incident occurring.

c) Data Dissemination

Once the data has been processed and prioritised by the traffic management centre it can then be disseminated using the various methods shown in Figure III.2. This can occur either directly or indirectly.

In the case of telephone, Teletext, and Videotex systems, dissemination can be achieved directly. Messages and map displays can be prepared and sent directly from the traffic management centre.

The special digital broadcasts required for the proposed vehicle-borne route guidance aids with radio up-dating of Class 7 could also be prepared and broadcast directly from the traffic management centre.

In the case of the media and other special broadcasting systems however, dissemination is usually indirect, i.e. via the publishers and broadcasters who will generally wish to compose messages for themselves and also decide if and when to broadcast them.

But whether the dissemination is direct or indirect, up-to-date information can be made available to the driver when he accesses these systems in the normal way -- although newspapers are unsuited to the dissemination of information about unpredictable and short-lived (few hours) incidents.

III.3. DIRECT TRAFFIC CONTROL SYSTEMS

III.3.1. Traffic control strategies

When using the driver information services described above, the responsibility for obtaining information, whether before or during the trip, falls to the driver who must usually take some action (make a telephone call or tune a radio) in order to receive the information. The direct traffic control systems of Classes 8 through 12 however, influence the driver directly by equipment mounted at the roadside. These systems can therefore expect to influence a higher proportion of drivers, although their effect is more local.

Table III.2 shows that the direct traffic control systems employ one of two control strategies: they either influence traffic by "setting mandatory impedances" at key positions in the network; or by "providing drivers with information" which describes a preferred course of action at a particular site. Systems which employ the second strategy have much in common with the driver information services of the previous section.

"Mandatory" and often variable "impedances" are employed in the UTC, tidal flow, and ramp metering systems of Classes 9 and 10 which generally rely on traffic signals to implement stop/go controls; and in the road pricing systems of Class 12 which impose charges on the use of particular sections of the network.

The Class 11 automatic route guidance systems "provide drivers with information". They indicate a preferred course of action at a particular site by providing drivers with junction by junction guidance over minimum path (e.g. distance, time, or cost) routes.

The Class 8 variable message sign and route control systems may employ either strategy. When the signs are used to set a speed restriction, they can effectively impose a mandatory impedance though speed indications are, in many cases, advisory. When used to direct traffic over an alternative route, they indicate a preferred course of action which, depending on the particular circumstances, may be mandatory or advisory.

Table III.2 shows that, in addition to route guidance and recommended speed information, the variable message sign and automatic route guidance systems may also be used to provide drivers with status messages, including: "incident type and location" and "delays", i.e. a description both of an incident, such as roadworks or an accident, and its consequences. Information on parking availability can also be given.

III.3.2. Data requirements

The data that must be gathered by the systems in order that these traffic control strategies can be put into effect are shown in Table III.3. All direct traffic control systems need to collect information on "measured traffic flows" and speeds.

For the systems of Classes 9, 10, and 12 which set mandatory impedances, this data is usually sufficient.

But for the systems of Classes 8 and 11 which give route guidance and hazard warning advice, additional data must be collected concerning "incident type", "reduced traffic capacity", and the "delays" caused.

Figure III.3 shows a general configuration for direct traffic control systems together with the essential elements of data gathering, processing, and dissemination. Information flows and the types of communication links used for transferring data between the various elements are also indicated.

a) Data Gathering

Sources of Data

With the exception of the Class 9 historic systems, all the direct traffic control systems depend upon data which is collected in real time. The data may be provided from data gathering networks set up for the driver information services and shown as "Other Information Sources" in Figure III.3, but more usually the data is collected by "automatic surveillance systems" which include road/weather sensors and vehicle detectors. CCTV is commonly used as a back-up to monitor known problem sites and to confirm the alarms from automatic warning systems.

These data are usually transmitted directly from the roadside sensors over private or leased lines to the traffic management centre where the information is centrally co-ordinated.

In Figure III.3 a separate source of data is shown from "vehicle sensors" which are used in the Class 11 automatic route guidance systems. The sensors monitor the time spent by vehicles in traversing the various links in the network. These data, together with the "destination" of each vehicle, are then transmitted to a central control computer via a special "communication infrastructure" which may, in principle, be shared by a Class 12 road pricing system.

Quality of Data

Data obtained by automatic surveillance systems and used directly by systems of Classes 10, 11, and 12 must usually be accepted without verification. Information from automatic weather and incident detection systems for use by the Class 8 variable message sign systems however, will often only be accepted after verification at the traffic management centre, frequently using CCTV.

b) Data Processing

Operation

In Figure III.3 data processing is shown to occur at a single traffic management centre where all information from all sources can be collated centrally. This is something of an ideal picture. In practice the direct traffic control systems tend to be treated as self-contained sub-systems within this larger organisation which is itself often distributed.

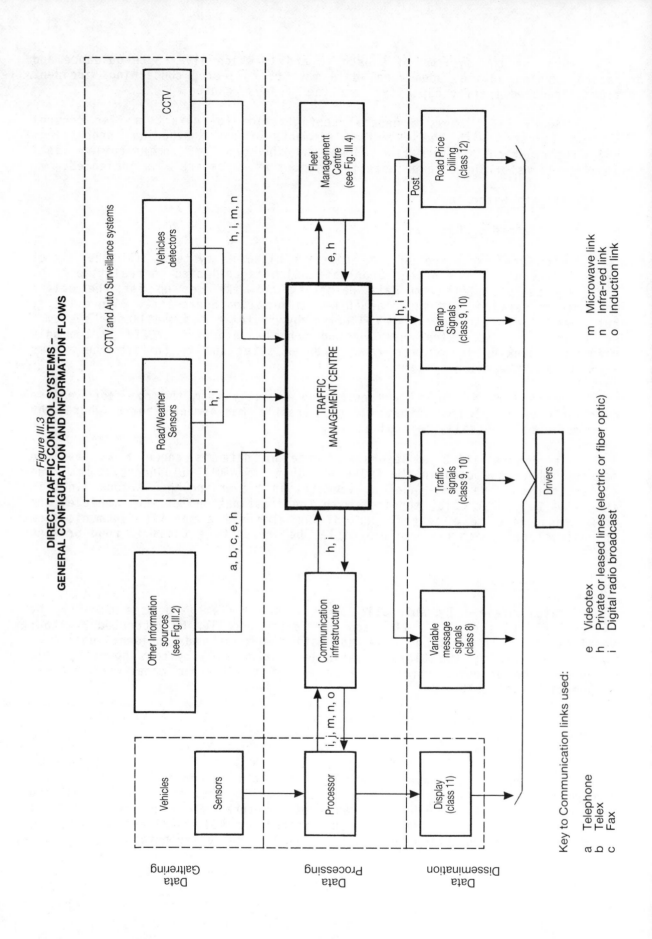

Figure III.3
**DIRECT TRAFFIC CONTROL SYSTEMS –
GENERAL CONFIGURATION AND INFORMATION FLOWS**

CCTV and Auto Surveillance systems

CCTV

Vehicles detectors

Road/Weather Sensors

Other Information sources (see Fig.III.2)

TRAFFIC MANAGEMENT CENTRE

Fleet Management Centre (see Fig. III.4)

Communication infrastructure

Road Price billing (class 12)

Ramp Signals (class 9, 10)

Traffic signals (class 9, 10)

Variable message signals (class 8)

Drivers

Post

Vehicles

Sensors

Processor

Display (class 11)

h, i, m, n

h, i

a, b, c, e, h

e, h

h, i

h, i

i, j, m, n, o

Data Gathering

Data Processing

Data Dissemination

Key to Communication links used:

a Telephone
b Telex
c Fax

e Videotex
h Private or leased lines (electric or fiber optic)
i Digital radio broadcast

m Microwave link
n Infra-red link
o Induction link

operate ge sign and route control systems of Class 8 usually
direct :mall networks or lengths of road and are controlled
comput r housed in the traffic management centre. The
and ma put from an associated automatic surveillance system
set th alarm to warn the traffic authority of the need to
no man lement a strategy to control the signs directly with
validat except in some systems where the operator just
by the setting of the message being then automatically done

and sel signal systems also operate over relatively small
meterin s, e.g. UTC and tidal flow systems in a town, ramp
separat motorway, and are also controlled from a (usually
the Cla in the traffic management centre. In the case of
fixed t ms, these run according to a pre-determined set of
pre-determined incident occurs when a more suitable (though again
) plan may be selected by a traffic controller. The Class 10
adaptive systems collect their own data from vehicle counting, queue, and
speed detectors distributed through the network. Traffic signal timings are
then co-ordinated by the control computer in such a way as to smooth the flow
of traffic as it redistributes itself around the sites of congestion. Until
recently, UTC and ramp metering systems have been treated in isolation.
Attempts are now being made in several countries to integrate them, i.e. to
co-ordinate the traffic in a town with the traffic entering and leaving the
motorway links. In these "distributed computer systems", data must be
exchanged and co-ordinated by the control computers for the separate systems.

The Class 11 automatic route guidance systems also collect their own
data, not only from sensors in the network, but also from equipped vehicles
which report their destinations and journey times on links. These data are
collected via a special communication infrastructure and co-ordinated by a
central computer in the traffic management centre. The system works
automatically to detect incidents, forecast traffic movements, and re-direct
individual vehicles by changing the guidance instructions given by the
roadside units. The Class 11 systems therefore provide network condition
information of use to the traffic management centre which can respond by
transmitting hazard warnings and advice to drivers on the approaches to
individual junctions. It seems likely that, as with the Class 10 adaptive
systems, these systems will operate both within towns and on rural feeder
networks. Distributed computer systems will therefore also be required here
-- especially if, as seems likely, it becomes necessary to integrate these
systems with the Class 10 adaptive signal systems.

The Class 12 road pricing systems rely on detectors situated at key
positions in the network to automatically sense the passing of individual
vehicles and to identify them. These data may then be passed over private or
leased lines to a central computer for collation and billing, or the charges
may be "remembered" by the vehicle unit for subsequent collection and
billing. The responsibility for running a system may fall to the traffic
management authorities or to a special organisation, but the police must be
involved to enforce the system which requires the compulsory fitting of
special units in vehicles.

Frequency of Updating

With the exception of the Class 9 historic systems, all the direct traffic control systems can operate in real time. Automatic surveillance enables these systems to respond within a few minutes, although some time is generally needed in which to establish that the data is genuine, and not a false alarm.

c) Data Dissemination

Data is disseminated directly in the Class 8 variable message sign systems which can show hazard warnings, speed restrictions, lane availability, alternative routes (i.e. route control), parking availability, etc.). The signs are controlled either directly or via a local micro-controller from the central control computer, usually over leased or private lines.

In the case of the Class 9 and 10 signalling systems, the system output is "experienced" by traffic as stop/go controls on the approaches to intersections and ramps. The traffic signals are co-ordinated by the central control computer and controlled by data which is transmitted to them either directly or via a local micro-controller, usually over leased or private lines.

In the Class 11 automatic route guidance systems, information such as hazard warnings or guidance instructions is transmitted from the central control computer to a special communication infrastructure usually over leased or private lines. The communication infrastructure is then used to communicate the information to individual vehicles where it is displayed to the driver using a special synthetic speech or visual display unit in his vehicle.

In the road pricing systems of Class 12 fixed or variable message signs at the side of the road are used to identify the position of, and the cost of crossing, each toll point. Drivers then "experience" the system in the form of bills which they receive through the mail at regular intervals.

III.4. PUBLIC TRANSPORT AND FLEET MANAGEMENT SYSTEMS

III.4.1. Traffic control strategies

The public transport and fleet management systems of Classes 13 and 14 operate within closed groups. Unlike the systems described previously, they are not directed at traffic in general, but rather at improving the efficiency of operating a particular fleet of vehicles and, in the case of public transport, taxis and freight operations, improving services for customers.

Table III.2 shows that these systems employ one of two strategies. The Class 13 (signal priority) systems "set mandatory roadside impedances" i.e. they control traffic signals so that special vehicles can be given priority. These systems are reserved exclusively for use by public transport and emergency (police, fire, or ambulance) service vehicles.

The Class 14 (vehicle fleet command and control) systems issue "fleet control instructions", i.e. they enable a controller to communicate with the individual vehicles in the fleet in order to provide a demand-responsive service.

Both strategies operate in real time and are often combined in systems for use by public transport and emergency services.

III.4.2. Data requirements

In order to realise these strategies, Table III.3 shows that the Class 13 and 14 systems both need information on "individual vehicle identification" i.e. they need to know the location and identity of the individual vehicles in the fleet. Some systems also need to know the "customer demand" for the service they provide and to know the "status" of each vehicle, i.e. its occupancy, schedule deviation, alarm status, and hence its relative ranking for receiving priority. Information on network conditions may also be required.

Figure III.4 shows a general configuration for these systems together with the essential elements of data gathering, processing, and dissemination. Data flows and the types of communication links used for transferring data between the various elements are also indicated.

a) Data Gathering

In the simplest Class 13 signal priority systems, vehicle identification and location data may be gathered directly by detectors at the roadside. The vehicles that are to receive priority must be equipped to activate these detectors which may then either: (i) activate a traffic signal directly each time an equipped vehicle passes; or (ii) communicate the demand for priority to the traffic management centre so that the signal can be controlled from there.

In more complex Class 13 systems, and particularly in those which are integrated with "fleet command and control" systems, data on vehicle location is obtained as described below for the Class 14 systems.

In the Class 14 systems, Figure III.4 shows that a communication infrastructure is used to provide 2-way communication, generally of both speech and data, between a "fleet management centre" and the drivers of the individual vehicles which make up the fleet. In this way the fleet management centre can learn the status of each vehicle and can respond to "customer demands" by sending specific instructions to the individual drivers in the fleet. The communication infrastructure may use a mobile radio to directly connect the controller with the drivers or it may, as with the Class 11 automatic route guidance systems, employ an intermediate infrastructure of roadside units.

One of three methods may be used so that the fleet management centre can learn the location of the vehicles (4):

Figure III.4
**PUBLIC TRANSPORT AND FLEET MANAGEMENT SYSTEMS –
GENERAL CONFIGURATION AND INFORMATION FLOWS**

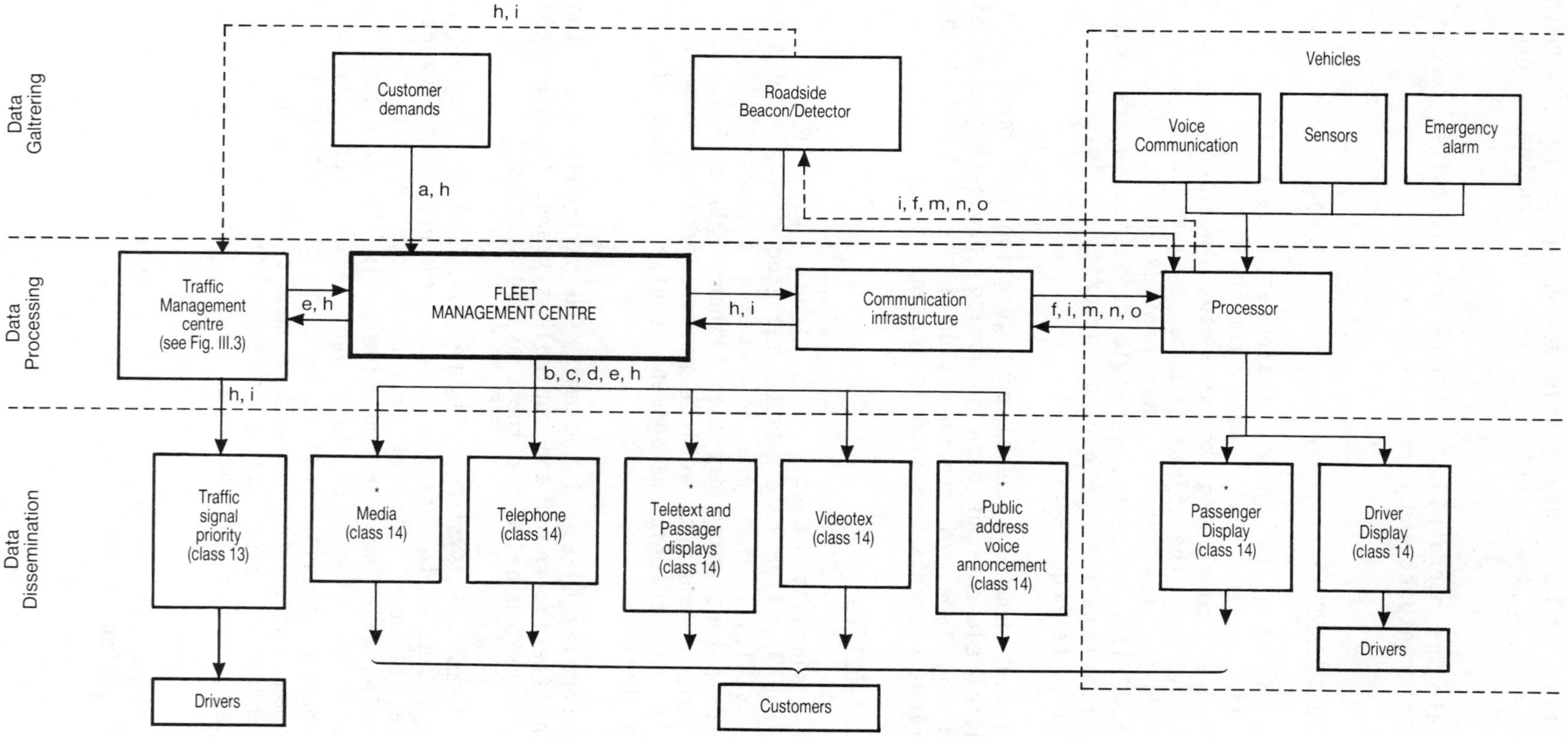

Vehicles

Emergency alarm

Sensors

Voice Communication

Processor

Driver Display (class 14)

Drivers

Passenger Display (class 14)

f, i, m, n, o

i, f, m, n, o

Communication infrastructure

Roadside Beacon/Detector

Public address voice anonncement (class 14)

Videotex (class 14)

h, i

Teletext and Passager displays (class 14)

Customers

Customer demands

a, h

FLEET MANAGEMENT CENTRE

b, c, d, e, h

Telephone (class 14)

Media (class 14)

e, h

Traffic Management centre (see Fig. III.3)

h, i

Traffic signal priority (class 13)

Drivers

h, i

Data Gathering

Data Processing

Data Dissemination

Key to Communication links used:

a   Telephone
b   Telex
c   Fax

d   Teletext
e   Videotex
f   Private Mobile radio/ˈphone

h   Private or leased line
i   Digital radio broadcast
m   Microwave link

n   Infra-red link
o   Induction link

Note: *Only relevant for public transport.

50

i) Dead reckoning -- in which the vehicle relies on an on-board navigation system (such as is used in the Class 7 systems) to deduce its position for itself;

ii) Beacons -- in which a vehicle's position is determined as it passes each of a number of position beacons distributed in the road network;

iii) Tri-lateration -- in which the vehicle's position is deduced with reference to radio transmissions which can either be transmitted from three or more fixed points in the network and detected on board the vehicle, or transmitted from the vehicle and detected at three or more fixed points.

When a dead reckoning system is used, the vehicle learns its position for itself and must report these data to the fleet control centre at regular intervals. Where beacons or tri-lateration techniques are used however, the vehicle can either deduce its position for itself or the fleet control centre can do so by monitoring the beacons or the radio receiving stations directly.

For vehicles such as buses and trams which follow fixed routes, beacons are frequently used. A measurement of distance driven allows the vehicle's position between beacons to be estimated with fairly high accuracy.

b) Data Processing

The Class 13 signal priority systems in which roadside detectors are monitored directly from a traffic management centre are able to respond automatically to demands for signal priority. In other systems the fleet management centre determines the demand patterns before it passes them to the traffic management centre.

But in all cases, the signals are controlled from the traffic management centre, in real time, either to extend the green time of an individual signal to favour a particular vehicle, e.g. a bus; or to co-ordinate the phases of a series of signals to give a "green wave" on a particular route, e.g. for an emergency service vehicle. Special plans may be devised to give public transport priority in special situations, e.g. during public events.

Other data gathered by the Class 14 fleet command and control systems is generally collected at the fleet management centre where it is displayed to a controller on a visual display unit in real time. He must then instruct the drivers as necessary in order to deploy the fleet to best meet the demands of customers.

c) Data Dissemination

All the Class 13 signal priority systems are controlled from a traffic management centre where they are generally integrated with a direct traffic control system, such as a UTC scheme of Class 9 or 10.

Data disseminated from the Class 14 systems is generally output directly from the fleet management centre, and includes: (i) instructions for drivers, which may be spoken, or displayed on a special vehicle display unit; and (ii) information for the use of customers. This describes service availability, timetables, modified arrival or departure times, and fares. Figure III.4 shows that the means for disseminating this information include: the media, telephone enquiry services, teletext and variable message sign displays, videotex services, and public address announcement systems. Similar information may also be given to passengers on special displays on board the vehicle itself.

REFERENCES

1. COST 30 BIS. Electronic traffic aids on major roads. Final Report. EUR 9835. Commission for the European Communities. Luxembourg, 1985.

2. MINISTERE DES TRANSPORTS. Systèmes d'aides à l'exploitation des transports publics urbains. Rapport de synthèse. CETUR. Paris, 1983.

3. EUCO-COST 30. European project on electronic traffic aids on major roads. EUR 7154. Commission for the European Communities. Luxembourg, 1981.

4. FOGY, W. Symposium on land vehicle navigation. Introduction. Deutsche Gesellschaft für Ortung und Navigation E.V. Münster, 1984.

5. JHK ASSOCIATES. Summary of the Conference on in-vehicle motorist information systems, held on 18th-20th September 1984. JHK Associates. Alexandria (Virginia), December 1984.

6. HUNT, PB et al. SCOOT. A traffic responsive method of co-ordinating signals. LR 1014. TRRL. Crowthorne, 1981.

Chapter IV

HUMAN FACTORS

The enormous growth of road traffic in recent years has prompted the responsible authorities not only to enlarge the existing infrastructure but also to look for new technological solutions for easing congestion. These developments are paralleled by substantial technological improvements to the vehicle. However, drivers have not changed, apart from becoming more accustomed to driving under congested traffic conditions, their physical and psychological limitations are still the same. The basic question is therefore whether the individual driver can keep pace with all these developments and changes that are presented to him.

IV.1. ERGONOMIC FACTORS RELATED TO THE DRIVING TASK

As the amount of traffic is steadily increasing, the driving task itself is absorbing a great deal of the driver's attention, especially as people tend to ignore safety margins, just to be able to keep on moving (1).

The amount of information the motorist has to "consume" is increasing as well. This goes for both visual and aural information: road signs, directional signs, road markings and information inside the vehicles, both aural (conventional radio) and visual (new in-vehicle devices under development).

IV.1.1 Considerations of perception

Careful attention should be paid not to exceed the perception limitations of motorists (2, 3, 17). This can be achieved by obeying the following rules:

-- try to limit the number of signs as much as possible;

-- do not give too much information on one sign;

-- try to use symbols instead of words, if possible (also of importance for foreign drivers);

-- give aural information in a concise way; do not divert the driver's attention for too long;

-- try to adhere to uniform solutions in order to improve recognition;

-- repeat information (aural information could be partially missed the first time and visual information is easily forgotten after a short time);

-- try to eliminate irrelevant information in order to reduce the amount of information drivers have to assimilate.

IV.1.2 Variable traffic signs

EUCO-COST 30 (Working Group 3) looked into the problems connected with variable traffic signs (4). From the results of various investigations, they derived the following information:

-- Since variable traffic signs relate to an immediate situation, observance of their contents is, in most cases, of the utmost importance to drivers;

-- They must be readily discernible, recognisable, and/or intelligible and legible;

-- Attracting the drivers' attention can be done by:

. The use of flashing lights,

. Sufficient light intensity in the case of internally illuminated signs, such as matrix signs,

. Signs of adequate dimension,

. The use of a surrounding dark screen to increase the contrast (some signs do not use internal illumination, but have luminescent points with a high level of retro-reflection).

A number of tests have been carried out on the legibility, discernibility and intelligibility of variable traffic signs (5, 6, 7, 19, 20).

An interesting conclusion was that in conditions of fog, matrix signs of the fibre optic type were more visible than conventional signs (both mounted overhead). A similar effect can be expected for fibre optic matrix signs mounted in the hard shoulder.

Also on the subject of pictograms, either used on their own or as an explanation of a speed recommendation, much research has been done. An interesting development is the Japanese system which uses light emitting diodes (LED's), instead of fibre optics (8).

IV.1.3. In-vehicle information system

Aural Information

Regarding aural information, EUCO-COST 30 (Working Group 4), commented that:

-- Messages should be kept as short as possible without losing the most important information;

-- The effect depends very much on the driver's knowledge of the road network;

-- The information should be given in a simple indicative way, in a fixed order.

Visual Information

Concerning visual information, investigations have to be made about its impact on driving behaviour (distraction issues), especially in view of the anticipated development of numerous in-vehicle visual information devices. This could lead to the use of head-up displays (as in aeronautics), instead of conventional cathode ray tube (CRT) displays, which are, in most States of the U.S.A, for example, prohibited inside vehicles.

IV.2 ACCEPTANCE OF THE SYSTEM BY DRIVERS

This section deals only with the qualitative aspects of driver acceptance, whereas quantitative aspects (measurements, surveys, etc.), will be covered in Section IV.5.

Acceptance of a system that advises motorists to change their normal pattern of behaviour, or asks them to obey certain restrictions, depends mostly on the reliability and credibility of such a system. Normally, most motorists -- especially commuters -- drive on the basis of their experience with the road network, traffic conditions and weather conditions. The information given to them must correspond to their normal practice, otherwise it will not be accepted. In other words, there must be a very good reason for asking them to change their normal pattern, otherwise they simply will not.

When building new systems, authorities should always bear in mind that the more complex and advanced a system is, more criticism from the users (motorists) can be expected. Also, one inconsistency can do more damage to the credibility than can be compensated for by ten accurate advisories.

IV.2.1 Attractiveness

If an alternative is offered (rerouting), it has to be kept in mind that such an alternative has to be attractive (saving of time, comfort). Furthermore, one has to consider that most people prefer staying on motorways when being rerouted.

The messages given should appeal to the existing knowledge of the drivers and should be given in a simple indicative way. The effect will always depend very much on the personal profit the driver perceives when following the indications or instructions.

IV.2.2 Form of the message

The message given to a motorist should be in such a form that he is not forced to look at or listen to an abundance of information and filter out the relevant points. In this respect, nationwide broadcasting information systems which oblige drivers to listen to their car radio all the time, in case there may be some relevant information for them, are not suitable.

Acceptance also depends very much on the way the message is presented. It is attractive only if the content applies to the road or weather situation the motorist may meet himself. For this reason the broadcasting of traffic information is often organised regionally.

The message should never be too long, as giving too many details irritates drivers and decreases the value of the message.

As has been pointed out above concerning the comparison between aural and visual messages, one could say that:

-- aural messages are easier to cope with, but are also forgotten sooner;

-- a visual message is there all the time, but looking at a CRT or other form of visual display may be dangerous while driving because of the distraction it could cause. There is also the possibility that the law may forbit CRT's in the driving compartment.

IV.2.3 Mandatory or advisory?

When giving indications to motorists, it is often questionable whether these should be mandatory or advisory. The difference is probably not as great as it seems; advisory measures for which there are sound reasons, are often better obeyed than mandatory measures without sound reason. Again, the motorist will judge himself, from his own experience. A good example of this is the use of the deflection arrow in the Dutch Motorway Control and Signalling Systems (MCSS) (11). Most drivers know it is advisory, yet it is the best observed symbol in the system. Mandatory speed signs along road works, however, are often very poorly observed, probably because the speed indicated is too low according to the motorist's own experience. Many drivers will conform best to a speed limit when it closely agrees with what they regard as reasonable.

IV.2.4. Elderly road users

When introducing new systems, it is also necessary to keep in mind that, according to recent studies (9), at the end of the century, perhaps one third of the road users will fall into the category of "elderly road users". Although elderly people do not seem to be unsafe drivers, diminished perceptive and decision-making abilities are a problem one has to consider.

IV.3. EXTENT OF SYSTEM INSTALLATION

This subject seems particularly interesting for in-vehicle systems, as for these systems not only the authorities responsible for traffic, but also motorists themselves must make investments. Also, the level of public acceptance is strongly dependent on the level of infrastructure offered by the authorities.

IV.3.1. How to get the most benefit?

When introducing a new in-vehicle system, the greatest problem is that the complete system is only sufficiently beneficial when:

a) the total infrastructure is installed; and
b) a sufficient number of motorists have the necessary equipment.

There seems to be a strong probability of a stalemate: the authorities being inclined to build the system only when enough motorists have the in-vehicle equipment, and the motorists being inclined to wait until the infrastructure is totally installed.

One way out of this situation is to make the in-vehicle equipment appealing enough so that it can sell commercially with sufficient success. In this regard, insofar as government financially support their national industries, this may enhance the development of a new commercial market.

Apart from government strategies, some automobile manufacturers are developing in-vehicle equipment on their own. This development could be called market driven.

IV.3.2. How to start?

EUCO-COST 30-bis (Group 1)(10) concluded:

-- From the engineering point of view it is preferable to install most intelligence at the roadside, but such a system could not be introduced gradually and requires large initial investments;

-- For a system to find acceptance it must be capable of being introduced gradually.

When building external communication systems, there is always the following choices to make:

a) Installation of a sparse system along many kilometers of roadway;

b) Installation of a very complete system on a short stretch of road.

It has to be considered that either choice, which obviously is related to financial possibilities, has a direct influence on the effectiveness the system will have.

A denser network can be made more attractive when the system is designed in such a way that it can serve a great number of tasks at the same time.

Some systems do not need infrastructure from the start; for instance, systems using a so-called electronic map can start in a more or less static i.e. non dynamic way.

IV.4 LEVEL OF DRIVER RESPONSE TO THE INDICATIONS SUPPLIED

The level of driver response is often checked by conducting driver opinion surveys (2, 10, 11, 12, 13, 14, 18). Other possibilities are measurements in the field (6, 10, 15), or laboratory experiments (7). While some investigations dealt with complete systems, most of them were carried out with the purpose of obtaining more information about some specific part of a system. For instance, much of the research has been carried out on the different aspects of matrix signs.

IV.4.1. Reaction of the public

When installing a control system, it should never be forgotten that people always want to be treated as individuals; they should not be given the impression that they cannot make their own decisions. Especially in urban networks, this means that installing automatic route guidance systems could be difficult, unless drivers can first be convinced that the system will benefit them personally.

Furthermore, if people are expected to follow instructions, these instructions have to be reasonable. As mentioned above, asking motorists to drive 30 km/hr at road works on a highway is unrealistic, and, of course, they will not obey.

Research about area broadcasting of traffic information (12) showed also that the level of response is related very strongly to the knowledge drivers have of the road network. Many people have little knowledge about the names of different junctions. It turned out to be necessary to use a standard form of message.

IV.4.2. Necessity of an explanation

In general it can be said that people want to know why something is asked of them. Again, speeds along road works can be taken as an example: in many countries 70 km/hr is shown, not for the safety of the driver but for the safety of the people working on the road. If the road seems clear and no workmen are present, it is understandable that people tend to disobey the indications.

It also appears that indicating the "why" should not be overdone. Showing the "road works" pictogram along with the recommended speed during the EUCO-COST 30 bis demonstration project in the Netherlands turned out to have no recognisable effect on speeds, probably because the reason was already clear enough.

Another interesting question is whether to warn (or inform) about the primary incident, or its results. For example, as soon as congestion occurred at the location of road works, it proved better to replace the road works pictogram by the queue pictogram at the first upstream set of speed limitations (16).

IV.4.3. Long term effect

Another important consideration is that the effects of many measures diminish after a certain period. People get used to a new type of measure and their own experience will play a more important role than the indications supplied.

Traffic authorities will always have to consider very carefully what is important for the motorist to know: in most cases general information about the weather, traffic situation and expected queues is enough and most people will not go to too much trouble to obtain this information. Again, one should always have a very good reason for asking people to modify their normal pattern of behaviour.

IV.5. ORGANISATIONAL PROBLEMS OF THE DATA GATHERING AND TRANSMITTING/DISSEMINATION CENTRES

In most cases, when organising a traffic management system, some kind of central organisation is needed. Only when the strategies are dealt with centrally can the measures be taken in a uniform way.

IV.5.1. Parties involved

The following differences exist between the interests of parties involved:

-- Motorists are mainly interested in all aspects that affect their trip (road and weather conditions, possibility of queues, etc.);

-- Road managers are interested in distributing the traffic evenly over their roads, easing maintenance, avoiding queues, etc;

-- The police are interested in the general traffic situation, as well as in locating incidents as soon as possible (essentially for safety purposes).

The relationship between road managers and the motorway police can cause problems. Both feel responsible for the motorway traffic from their own standpoint. When a complex traffic control system is being used by both parties, it is necessary to have a clear agreement about the operation of the system. Some existing systems show that such a dual control, via one system, is possible.

IV.5.2. Operation

No matter what the level of automation of a system is, traffic accidents always need verification on the spot. Also, road managers need contact with many other parties (maintenance team, police, meteorologists, etc.), as can be seen in Figures III.2 and III.3). Sometimes information has to be provided for local radio stations, videotex transmissions, etc. There may also be a lot of information coming in that can only be translated into messages via operator intervention. This means that in most traffic control centres it is necessary to have personnel (operators) in the control centre. It depends on the complexity and the number of tasks, whether this should be continuous or only for a number of hours each day.

All information related to the infrastructure must continuously be kept up-to-date. This could mean, for example, making changes to a system data base for statistical purposes (invesment planning), or checking shifts in the adequacy of the central system to the demand pattern.

In some cases it is necessary for different (regional) control centres, doing the same kind of work, to exchange information. The corresponding organisational problems can lead to formal agreements between the parties involved. For example, in the Metropolitan Toronto area, the Freeway Traffic Management on Highway 401 Project Control Centre (under the jurisdiction of Ontario Province) will be linked to the Metropolitan Toronto Traffic Control Centre (city jurisdiction), and the Ontario Provincial Police Center. Incident detection and management procedures have been jointly elaborated to set the responsibility of each authority.

IV.5.3. Reliability

For safety and driver acceptance purposes, it is worthwhile to expend much effort on the reliability of a control system. One way of doing this is to ensure that failure in a part of the system can never bring the whole system down. For instance, if in the Dutch Motorway Control and Signalling System, the communication to an outstation fails the outstation will keep its legends commanded from the central computer, but will also generate its own AID (Automatic Incident Detection) warning messages, if necessary.

IV.6. LEGAL PROBLEMS
(OBLIGATIONS OR RECOMMENDATIONS, COMPULSORY VEHICLE EQUIPMENT, ETC.)

An interesting question may be whether the messages given to motorists should be mandatory or advisory, but as has been shown in Section IV.2.3, the effect of a system does not depend entirely on this choice. The credibility of the message might have a much greater effect.

IV.6.1. Obligations

It is clear that it would be extremely difficult to require people to install in-vehicle equipment for traffic or route information purposes. First, supervision would be almost impossible (except in some small, closed areas), and secondly it would be impossible to check the use people make of it. Languages used could also present a problem with in-vehicle aural equipment. The use of digital codes and synthesized speech could be a solution to this problem. Sometimes the use of video displays in the driver compartment is forbidden.

An interesting point is that in most countries, it is not essential to have good hearing; deaf people can get a driving licence. As with elderly road users, because of the so-called "compensation phenomena", these drivers are not a priori considered more dangerous.

IV.6.2. Obligations or recommendations

External visual signs can be advisory or mandatory; sometimes the police, not the traffic authorities, make this choice which may enable them to repress people who are ignoring the indications. Directional signs are in most cases advisory. Although there are cases where there is no other alternative than the route advised, it is quite reasonable to leave the risk of not observing the advice to the motorist himself. Directional signs can be individualised by presenting additional in-vehicle information (ALI, etc.).

Speed signs may be advisory or mandatory. In systems used for accident or queue warning, it seems wiser to use advisory (or recommended) maximum speeds. First, in situations like these, speed indications may change rather rapidly, both in time and position. Second, it is not necessary to check compliance during dense traffic situations or during queuing.

From a practical point of view, it is clear that in-vehicle indications can only be of an advisory nature, whereas indications that are mandatory should always be installed along the road.

IV.6.3. Legislation

When using new types of signs, it may be necessary to make certain changes to traffic legislation. For instance, the use of matrix signs led to the necessity to approve the use of white symbols on a black background, something that was not foreseen in the Vienna Convention. In the Netherlands, the use of some new experimental pictograms during a demonstration project, promoted the introduction of new warning signs in the Dutch Highway Code. In Germany also, mandatory signs of the matrix type were introduced in the StVO (the German Highway Code). It is very important that changes like these are not limited to one country only, but that there is uniformity throughout Europe. For this reason the new pictograms were presented to the European Conference of Ministers of Transport (ECMT) committee on signs.

IV.6.4. Privacy

A final, but not less important point: when introducing new electronic equipment, people are always afraid that this will influence their privacy. For this reason, there is a rather strong objection against devices such as electronic licence plates and road pricing devices, etc.

In some countries, like France, the law protects the individual's privacy against the damages coming from data base disclosures, or inter-connections. Some techniques, like prepaid electronic transport fee cards, can avoid the use of such controversial means as home billing, or direct account billing. Such protection of the individual liberty and privacy should certainly be investigated and extended in view of limiting the ever growing influence of electronics and informatics in the life of people in industrialised countries.

REFERENCES

1. VAN TOORENBURG, JAC. The driver and busy motorway traffic. Dienst Verkeerskunde. The Hague, 1983.

2. LABIALE, G. Approche psycho-ergonomique des systèmes d'information et de guidage routier des conducteurs automobiles. IRT/CERNE. Lyon, 1984.

3. DUDECK, CL, HUTCHINSON, RD. Manual on real-time motorist information displays. FHWA. Washington, 1984.

4. EUCO-COST 30. Final report. Commission of the European Communities. Brussels, 1980.

5. TRRL. A new motorway signal. LR 1075 Transport and Road Research Laboratory. Crowthorne, 1982.

6. HESS. MIN. FUER WIRTSCHAFT UND TECHNIK. Wechsel-Wegweisung, Busspuren und Richtgeschwindigkeiten. Erfahrungen in Hessen. Hess. Min. fuer Wirtschaft und Technik., 1978.

7. TRRL. Recognition distances and understanding of legends on an experimental motorway signal. LR 500. Transport and Road Research Laboratory. Crowthorne, 1973.

8. OECD. Variable information board employing LED and solar battery. OECD Seminar on Micro-Electronics for Road and Traffic Management. Traffic Bureau National Police Agency. Tokyo, 1984.

9. OECD. Traffic safety of elderly road users. Road Transport Research Programme. OECD. Paris, 1985.

10. EUCO-COST 30-BIS. Final Report. Commission of the European Communities. Brussels, 1985.

11. DIENST VERKEERSKUNDE. Evaluation of the external effects of the motorway control and signalling system. Dienst Verkeerskunde, The Hague, 1982.

12. BOER, LC. How well can Dutch motorway drivers apply the traffic news to their own travel? Institute for Perception (TNO). Soesterberg, 1983.

13. CARRE, JR. Etude exploratoire sur les choix d'itinéraires dans un réseau routier comportant une autoroute à accès contrôlés. ONSER. Paris, 1980.

14. BAST. Grundlagen und Moeglichkeiten der Nützung Sprachlicher Informationssysteme im Kraftfahrzeug. Bundesanstalt für Strassenwesen, FAT. No 39. Bergisch Gladbach, 1984.

15. TRRL. Automatic speed warning sign -- Hampshire trials. LR 1118. Transport and Road Research Laboratory. Crowthorne, 1983.

16. EUCO-COST 30-BIS. Final report of the demonstration project group. Commission of the European Community. Brussels, 1984.

17. RIEMERSMA, JBJ. et al. Human factors considerations relevant for highway information systems. OECD Seminar on Electronics and traffic on major roads. OECD. Paris, 1985.

18. ANDREW, C. An interview survey of motorway driver information requirements and signal understanding. LR 742. TRRL. Crowthorne, 1977.

19. LOTENS, WA. and VAN LEEUWEN, RE. A set of digits for matrix lightboxes. Institute for perception (TNO). Soesterberg, 1976.

20. VALETON, JM. and VOS, JJ. The legibility of matrix lightboxes in fog compared with overhead signs. A theoritical study. Soesterberg, 1979.

Chapter V

FUTURE DIRECTIONS

Although traffic control is over a half century old, it is only during the last two decades that systems were developed which were capable of automatic monitoring and control of traffic in large networks. The advent of the process control computer (the mini) and the use of telephone lines for the transmission of digital information were the main reasons for this achievement. The next two decades will see even greater advances in traffic control due to the spectacular developments which are taking place in computers and communications, as well as a variety of other technologies. These will lead to significant improvements in the performance of conventional types of systems, as well as the development of entirely new classes of systems, which will result in a more efficient and safe use of the roadway system as a whole (1).

These technological developments will appear at the right time when profound changes in the traffic environment can be anticipated, due to the growth and distribution of traffic demand and to the perceptions and expectations of the roadway user. In addition to coping with an expected annual growth of 2 to 3 per cent in urban traffic demand in most industralised countries, perhaps as much as 25 per cent of which will be heavy vehicles and buses, there will be a need to increase the efficiency of the movement of goods and services throughout the roadway system, as well as address problems such as parking and the rights of pedestrians and the elderly. The advent of a new society where all kinds of information will be available nearly anywhere and at any moment will stress the need for good road information.

As a result, public authorities will have to define clear policies, i.e. take a position on such things as promotion of public transit, restrictions on the use of the roadway, the amount of new construction, energy conservation, protection of the environment, enforcement of traffic laws, etc. These policies will shape the goals and type of future traffic management systems.

In this Chapter, we will, therefore, successively examine the new technologies and the future strategies in the field of dynamic traffic management.

V.1. NEW TECHNOLOGIES

The underlying technologies upon which process control systems depend are developing rapidly, and this is true of traffic control systems in particular. Computers (processors) and communications are the dominant technologies, but developments in sensor and display technologies, as well as control theory, will be equally important in the development of future traffic management and control systems.

V.1.1. Processing

The continuing rapid development of new processors due to advances in VLSI (Very Large Scale Integration) technology is the factor which will have the greatest influence on the future development of new traffic management systems. The so-called super minicomputer of today has virtually the same power of a mainframe computer of a few years ago. This will open up an enormous scope for the development of sophisticated programs which could carry out a wide variety of tasks, such as real-time simulation and optimisation of large traffic systems. In addition, there are fault-tolerant and self-repairing processors becoming available which will improve the reliability of traffic management systems.

At the other end of the scale, the rapid development of the microprocessor will present increasing opportunities for enhancing the performance of existing systems and for developing new applications. The microprocessor-based traffic signal controller is a good example of the former. An example of the latter is the use of microprocessors for a variety of purposes, including in-vehicle navigation and information systems. The 16 bit microprocessor is being applied for such applications and the 32 bit microprocessor is on the horizon. These machines, which are equivalent in power to yesterday's minicomputers, present opportunities for truly amazing advances in many different areas within the next decade.

Special purpose processors based on VHSIC (Very High Speed Integrated Circuits) technology and parallel processing techniques are finding application in a number of areas of interest to traffic management, including traffic simulation and image processing.

Advances in computer memory and mass (data) storage devices will also have significant influence on the development of future systems. Already, the 1 Megabyte RAM (Random Access Memory) chip is becoming available through recent improvements in VLSI technology, and even larger chips will be made available in the future at relatively low cost. Bubble memory will likely find increasing application as a mass storage device in the future because it is non-volatile and, unlike electromechanical storage devices like disc drives, is able to tolerate a harsh physical environment such as is found in the typical motor vehicle. Perhaps the most spectacular memory device presently under development, at least in terms of its enormous data storage capacity, is the CD-ROM, or compact disc read-only memory. Using laser technology, a disc less than 6 inches in diameter will be able to store over 500 Megabytes of information, or enough capacity to store a digital map of every highway and street in the United States and Canada, or Europe. Clearly, such developments will have a major impact on future traffic management systems.

V.1.2. Communications

The wide variety of communications currently used for traffic management will be evident from Figures III.2, III.3 and III.4 (see Chapter III), which show the generalised configurations and information flows for the three categories of systems defined in this report. These include a combination of public, private and leased systems and involve the transmission of voice, data and video information over various types of communication systems. Most of these systems are based on mature technology, but there are some developments which will have an impact on traffic management systems in the future.

Radio systems are of particular interest, especially those which ensure digital data dissemination. Though most are presently ground-based, hybrid systems using satellite communications are a possibility for the future. These systems have potential application to traffic management in a number of different areas.

The 1-way digital radio system has possibilities for broadcasting traffic and other information to vehicles equipped with suitable receivers. It can also be used to broadcast information to a number of fixed remote locations such as, for example, to variable message signs or other traffic control devices, or from data collection outstations to a control centre. In each case, the structure of the message is encoded preselectively so that each outstation (fixed or mobile) receives its intended message.

The 2-way digital radio system also has possibilities. The so-called point-to-multipoint radio data systems are being used for a variety of purposes, including process control (e.g. remote control of water irrigation systems). They use various polling and message switching techniques, depending on the number of outstations and the data rate requirements. These systems certainly have potential application for transmission of control and surveillance information in area and motorway traffic control systems, and perhaps also for some mobile applications. Some of these systems operate at microwave frequencies and are, thus, limited to line-of-sight applications (e.g. automatic toll collection). Getting the necessary spectrum allocation is a problem, as it is for all radio systems in this day and age.

Of the various types of land mobile radio systems available, cellular systems offer the most cost effective utilisation of the available spectrum. They will, therefore, be an attractive choice where many vehicles are involved. For this reason, public cellular systems (those connected to the public switched telephone network) may turn out in the long run to have a greater impact on the development of future traffic management systems than any other means of communication. Although they are initially being used mainly for voice communications, there is an increasing need for data communications for mobile office applications. A digital cellular radio network covering the whole of Europe will be implemented in 1990. Such systems can, however, only handle a limited number of vehicles at a time.

This need for data communications has fostered the development of a new generation of intelligent modems which use sophisticated error correction techniques to ensure data integrity on moving vehicles. These are now available and the cost is dropping rapidly as the market expands. The "mobile office" is, indeed, becoming a practical reality for many commercial purposes, and the more general "mobile information system" concept is waiting in the wings.

Another technology which will influence the development of future traffic management systems is fibre optics communications. While it is presently best suited for trunking applications, multidrop applications should become very cost effective in the near future, especially for motorway systems but also in towns, where the future fibre optic TV network could be used for data transmission. The high video quality and band width, and the low maintenance costs make fibre an attractive alternative to coaxial cable.

The development of new low cost solid state microwave electronics is making microwave communications a sound choice for many applications. The successful use of infrared communications will depend on improving the reliability of transmission under foggy conditions and reducing cost. These two technologies are likely to develop for data dissemination using roadside beacons used by vehicle-borne and automatic route guidance systems.

International standards are presently being established for the communications infrastructure of the 21st Century. This involves all-digital communications and an attempt at rationalisation of existing services into an integrated services digital network (ISDN).

V.1.3. Sensors

The level of performance which can be achieved from a traffic management system at any given time is fundamentally dependent on the amount and quality of information available on conditions existing on the roadway system. Some of this information is, nowadays, gathered by observers like police patrols, etc. and generally concerns parameters like incidents, queuing or road/weather conditions. Such information sources will exist for a long time for many reasons, one of them being that police patrols are needed for safety purposes. However, sensors for the measurement of traffic conditions will develop more and more because of the growing size and dynamics of systems, and an increasing demand will be placed on their performance and reliability. Sensors for the automatic measurement of road weather conditions will also probably be more and more developed due to safety and maintenance concerns (17).

The vehicle detector, which provides information from which the basic traffic flow variables (flow rate, speed, density, queue length, etc.) can be estimated, is generally regarded as the weakest link in the system. A wide variety of detectors have been developed, including ultrasonic, radar, magnetometer and magnetic induction loop detectors.

The loop detector has been by far the most successful, although the other types are still used, especially in locations where the loop detector may not operate satisfactorily, such as in tunnels or on steel bridges. However, despite numerous improvements in its performance (e.g. self-tuning) and installation, the loop detector is difficult and inconvenient to install, and has a relatively high incidence of failure, particularly in areas with a severe winter. It generally leaves much to be desired but there is no replacement on the immediate horizon, although there are a number of developments which show some promise.

In the short term, there have been some improvements in ultrasonic and radar detectors (Japan), and the new self-powered vehicle detector (SPVD) being developed in the United States shows promise. This detector is a magnetometer type with a low power radio link to the roadside. It is installed in a single cylindrical hole in the center of a lane and operates for years between battery changes. Simplicity of installation and the fact that there is no physical connection to the roadside make it an attractive alternative to loops if the price can be made competitive.

Apart from conventional detectors, which collect data at a point, one can imagine that there will be a considerable development of what can be called area traffic detectors, based on video picture collection (the camera being placed near the ground or on-board a satellite). Current developments under way in a number of countries of a vision system detector based on pattern recognition and image processing techniques show considerable promise. This could have important implications since such a detector can potentially gather traffic information over a wide area and, thus, provide traffic density and other types of information (such as queues, turning movements, etc.) which is difficult to derive from conventional detectors. The technology to develop these systems is rapidly becoming available. Although the requirement for real-time image processing is formidable, special parallel VHSIC processors are available, and local (at the camera) rather than central processing will be feasible. High resolution solid state television cameras are also available, and it is very likely that an integrated camera/processor vehicle detector will be on the market in a few years, although the full capabilities of such a detector may not be realised for some time.

Vehicle identification is a requirement for some applications such as automatic real-time origin-destination and travel times collection, road pricing and automatic toll collection. Special sensors have been developed for this purpose: Hong Kong road pricing (one-way vehicle-to-road link, based on electromagnetic transmission), and AUTO-SCOUT, a German automatic route guidance system (two-way link, based on infrared transmission), for example. In the future, it is possible that the vision system detector could perform the vehicle identification function by reading licence plate numbers or by identifying special classes of vehicles for signal priority, enforcement (e.g. overweight vehicles) or other purposes.

Vehicles equipped with such two-way communication links (mobile radio-telephones and CB radios being the first wide spread ones), although not strictly sensors, can be used as roving traffic probes to enhance the data collection of traffic management systems, and this is one of the objectives for the various systems which are under development.

V.1.4. Displays

In the context used here, displays are those devices which communicate dynamic visual information to the travelling public either before or during their trips. In the case of the driver, this information may come either from the roadside or from within his vehicle.

As far as pretrip information displays are concerned, it is unlikely that television for teletext and videotex messages will be replaced for some time to come. However, the quality of the graphics will greatly improve with two new developments on the not too distant horizon - high resolution TV and fibre optics networks.

Variable message signs (VMS) in one form or another have been used for many years to convey messages from the roadway to the driver. They are also used by transit authorities to provide routing and schedule information to prospective passengers. Apart from the conventional technologies such as incandescent bulb matrix, electromechanical roller and rotating panel, new technologies using optical fibres and, more recently, light-emitting diodes, are being increasingly used and developed. Laser-based and holographic optical systems are also being investigated. In Europe, some normalisation problems occur in this respect because those systems generally display signs as bright symbols on dark backgrounds, which is in conflict with the Vienna Convention.

The VMS is a critical element in many present day traffic management systems but it may well become less important in the future as more vehicles are equipped with mobile information systems (in-vehicle technology with at least a receive capability) and information can be conveyed to the driver by in-vehicle displays or other means. Until this happens, which will truly lead traffic management into a new era, the VMS in more or less its present form will be used for some time to come.

If present trends continue, the automobile of the future will be ablaze with various types of electronic displays, which raises serious concerns about the ability of the driver to drive safely with so many distractions. The use of a CRT display while driving is of particular concern. Since this is the basis of most of the existing or proposed automobile navigation systems (following a route on an electronic map), considerable research effort is being devoted to finding an alternative way of communicating the necessary information to the driver. Aural communication using synthetic speech is now possible with new voice synthesis chips, but possibly a more promising approach is to borrow head-up display technology from the aircraft industry. In fact, this is being done and several head-up display systems are under development for use in the automobile. A new type using a holographic optical system shows particular promise.

V.1.5. Control theory and techniques

The three fundamental considerations in developing any control system are observability, controllability and stability. They are useful for getting a qualitative understanding of the problems to be faced in the development of large, complex control systems such as the integrated traffic management system of the future.

Observability relates to the ability to measure the state of the process or system which is being controlled and is primarily dependent on the amount and quality of information which is fed back from various sensors located throughout the system. This information provides a description of the system so that appropriate controls can be applied. The more dynamic and sophisticated the control desired, the greater the amount and quality of the information required. Since this is the direction in which traffic management is headed, it is clear that traffic surveillance, and the sensors required to collect the necessary data, will present a major challenge for new systems. Hopefully, this will be met by the development of new and improved sensors.

Controllability is an important consideration which relates to the question of whether or not, given existing constraints, it is even possible to control a system at all, regardless of what type of controls are used. This is a particularly important issue in assessing traffic management requirements since there are often locations, times or situations in which nothing really can be done to prevent or alleviate severe congestion -- in other words, the situation is uncontrollable. It also relates to the effectiveness of a particular control strategy. If, for example, fewer drivers than anticipated react to a particular diversionary message, the strategy will fail.

Stability concerns the possibility that the control system may in fact make the situation worse than before by applying controls which produce a destabilising positive feedback effect rather than the negative feedback which is required for stability. This has not been a major concern in the development of traffic management systems in the past, but there are indications (see Section V.2.2) that stability will be an important consideration in the development of the more sophisticated traffic management strategies which will be used in the future.

In recent years there have been significant advances in control theory on a number of different fronts, and many of these are applicable to traffic management and control. Although some present-day systems use advanced control techniques, in some ways theory is ahead of application. However, it seems likely that the relatively enormous computing power becoming available, at both the high and low ends of the scale, will be an incentive for application of more advanced control theory and techniques in the future.

A control system can be classified according to the level of sophistication of the type of control used. This is illustrated in Figure V.1 for a generalised traffic control system, where each additional level represents an increased capability of the system to more accurately compensate for changing conditions.

Most traffic control systems today operate at the second level, although there are some arterial signal systems and motorway traffic management systems which still operate at the first level. Virtually all area traffic control systems use optimal control in one form or another. Most use time-of-day or traffic responsive selection of pre-stored timing plans, which are generated off-line using one of the standard signal timing optimisation programs. These programs compute timing plans for a particular set of traffic conditions and use an assumed model for the traffic flow process. The plans, thus, gradually become out of date and must be recalculated periodically, a task which is frequently neglected in practice. In addition, these systems cannot respond to short term changes in the traffic which is frequently neglected in practice.

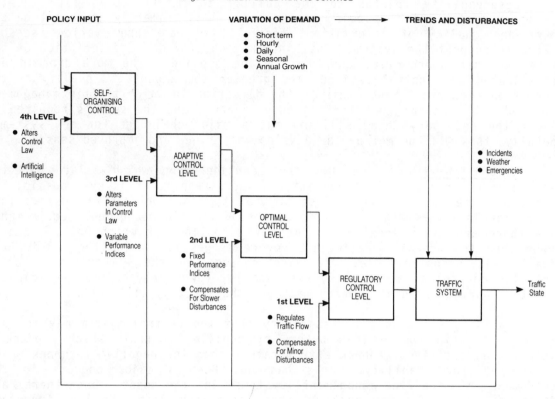

Figure V.1 MULTI-LEVEL TRAFFIC CONTROL

There are a number of systems of this type which overcome this problem by using on-line optimisation in conjunction with a traffic flow predictor to automatically adjust signal timings to reflect changing demands. They can also compensate for relatively short term variations in traffic demand (of the order of 30 minutes). The UTCS Second Generation in the United States and RTOP in Toronto are typical of these systems. The so-called 1.5 Generation Systems which are presently under development are somewhere between the two. In all of these systems, the traffic flow model used in the optimisation algorithm is fixed and does not account for basic changes in traffic behaviour which occur over time.

Next is the adaptive control level in which systems automatically alter the parameters (but not the structure) of their traffic flow model to account for changes in traffic behaviour. SCOOT (Coventry), SCATS (Sydney) and PRODYN (Toulouse) fall into this category, and represent the state-of-the-art at this time.

Future systems will operate at the fourth level shown in Figure V.1. This is the self-organising control level in which the traffic control system will alter the basic form of the control law (which involves the traffic model) to respond to changing conditions and circumstances, reflecting not only changes in traffic demand and behaviour but also different control policies. This type of control will be particularly important for integrated urban traffic management. It is fertile ground for the application of artificial intelligence techniques (expert systems, fuzzy logic, etc.) (2).

Motorway traffic management systems, in a sense, have not advanced as far as area traffic management systems. Although many are highly traffic responsive, virtually all are still operating at the first level of control shown in Figure V.1. A typical ramp metering system (3,18), for example, essentially regulates traffic flow and does not globally optimise the system according to some overall criterion, such as minimum travel time. Unfortunately, the traffic flow process is very complex (nonstationary, nonlinear, stochastic), and represents a challenge even for modern control theory. However, the development of improved freeway traffic flow models (4) and the application of modern nonlinear optimal control theory shows promise that more effective freeway traffic management systems can be developed in the future (5).

There have been significant advances in other areas as well. Optimal estimation theory based on Kalman filtering has become highly developed in recent years. It can accommodate nonstationary processes and is finding increasing application for estimating basic traffic parameters from vehicle sensor data. The theory of hierarchical (or decentralised) control systems, and particularly that dealing with decentralised adaptive control of interconnected systems, will be relevant to integrated traffic management (see Section V.2.4.).

Co-operative systems is another area of active research which could find application for integrated control of systems located in different jurisdictions (6). They allow each system to operate co-operatively toward a common goal and yet retain a certain degree of autonomy for reasons of self-interest (7).

Developments in artificial intelligence have potential application in the operation of traffic management centres. Knowledge-based expert systems, which could capture the collective knowledge and experience of system operators, would be a very useful operational tool. In fact, since human operators have demonstrated performance which is often superior to an automatic control system in some situations, it is conceivable that an expert system could eventually act as the main controlling element, with human intervention taking place only under unusual circumstances. Such an expert system is being developed for tackling oversaturated periods in the centre of Paris (8).

Another area related to artificial intelligence which is finding application is fuzzy logic. A traffic signal controller based on fuzzy logic was found to outperform a typical traffic actuated controller (9).

Finally, continuing investigations in the field of automatic incident detection using new techniques and algorithms must be mentioned especially under free flow traffic conditions (19).

V.2. FUTURE STRATEGIES AND APPLICATIONS

From the foregoing review of new technology, it is evident that there is tremendous potential for the development of a new generation of traffic management systems in the future. Ideally, the following issues could be prophesied: processing power will be available in abundance, communications will be more cost effective and may even extend to individual vehicles, improved detectors will provide comprehensive surveillance capabilities, real-time simulation and expert systems will be available to assist the operator and all systems will employ real-time adaptive decentralised optimal control. These all may, indeed, come to pass, but there are many obstacles which must be overcome before this can become a reality, such as the lack of standardization, the "software bottleneck", the scarcity of electromagnetic spectrum for radiocommunications, etc.

In the following, implications of both the development of new technologies and the above-mentioned obstacles are discussed, speculating on the evolution of dynamic traffic management until the end of the century.

V.2.1. Driver information systems

Future developments in driver information systems will have to deal with the deficiencies which exist in many present systems. To maintain credibility with the public, it will be necessary to ensure that all information is accurate, timely and relevant to the driving circumstances and drivers' needs. This is certainly not always the case today, where the collection of information from various sources and its distribution to the driving public is still often a disorganised and inefficient process.

Probably the most significant development expected in the near future is the integration and consolidation of all the various sources of traffic information at a central point (traffic management centre), from which it will be transmitted to the driving public by various means, as shown symbolically in Figure III.2. While this is already being done to some degree in a number of large urban centres, it is the exception rather than the rule. As a matter of fact, if the organisational problem is not solved, sophisticated techniques will be of no use in this field of driver information (10).

In some countries, most of the traffic information is prepared and disseminated by private organisations. In some cases, a commercial radio station may operate their own service using information from their own observers (aircraft, etc.) and from the authorities (police, traffic management centres, etc.). In other cases, a private company may provide a traffic information service to a number of client commercial radio stations. In general, participation by the private sector should be encouraged because competition tends to ensure quality service with minimum burden on the taxpayers, provided that there should not be direct information dissemination to the public (without first going through a traffic management centre), which is not always the case presently. This, and other similar problems, will have to be resolved without discouraging participation from the private sector.

The availability of digital radio broadcasting will overcome the major drawback of existing commercial radio broadcasting of traffic information (except some local systems like HAR in the United States) where all drivers are addressed regardless of whether the message is relevant to their particular need or not. Operating with vehicles equipped with a suitable radio receiver, this system can broadcast over a large area and yet be selective in the dissemination of messages to certain groups of drivers, and possibly even to individual drivers. Specially encoded preselected messages would be used, and it would be possible in the future to present the same message in several languages by means of a digitally actuated voice synthesiser or a pictogram display located in the vehicles. Allocation of spectrum and lack of communications standards are critical issues which must be resolved before manufacturers are induced to develop the necessary in-vehicle equipment for these systems to become commercially viable.

Self-contained in-vehicle navigation systems are beginning to appear on the market. Most have an electronic map for navigation purposes, and locate their position by a variety of techniques, including radio trilateration (anticipated use of satellites), map-matching and dead reckoning. In the next few years these systems will likely be used mainly in luxury automobiles and special vehicles (delivery vehicles, etc.), but by the next decade owners will be able to afford them as well. This raises some questions for the public authorities concerning the potential utilisation of these systems for driver information and route guidance applications, through the implementation of a one-way or two-way communications link. The common digital radio broadcast channel being proposed for Europe could be used for providing route guidance information to vehicles with in-vehicle navigation systems as well as broadcasting conventional traffic information to other vehicles. It would be mainly used to up-date electronic maps and provide dynamic route guidance information. Standardization of message structure and vehicle interfaces, which is required to encourage manufacturers to produce the necessary hardware, is the critical issue here.

Other alternatives for establishing communications with the vehicle are likely to develop as well, namely roadside beacons based on microwave, infrared or ultrasonic technologies. They will ensure functions such as relocation for drifting autonomous location systems, dissemination of local traffic or services information and of digital local map updates, automatic on-the-move toll collection (especially needed in urban areas), etc.

V.2.2. Direct traffic control systems

Traffic control systems for urban networks and motorways have become well established in industrialised countries to cope with the congestion caused by what appears to be an ever increasing number of motor vehicles. As this situation continues, there will be increasing demands placed on these systems to maintain and, if possible, improve the mobility conditions offered to people, goods and services. This will be a challenge, but advances in traffic control technology show promise that this could, indeed, be achieved.

Conventional fixed-time control strategies based on historic traffic flow data are giving way to those that are more dynamic in their response to changing conditions. This is true for both area and motorway traffic control. Dynamic traffic responsive control strategies have already been developed for both types of systems (20).

There is a growing realisation that current area traffic control strategies tend to reinforce the existing patterns of traffic movement rather than encouraging possible alternatives to these patterns (11). Whenever an improvement is made on a particular route, the improvement quickly disappears because more drivers will soon learn to choose the improved path for their journeys. This will lead to the need for further improvement, which in turn, attracts more traffic. In other words, the present strategies have an inherent positive feedback effect which tends to perpetuate the concentration of traffic on major routes and, thus, the imbalance between them and other less heavily trafficked routes (in networks where oversaturation is not the usual situation). Future dynamic traffic management strategies should, therefore, implement signal timing controls which encourage traffic to re-route, so as to distribute it more evenly throughout the network under normal and incident conditions.

This is one aspect of the more general concept that signal timing can be used to effectively 'manage' traffic in a network rather than simply controlling it in the conventional sense. This implies that systems in the future will no longer be designed with maximum mobility solely in mind. Other measures of effectiveness will have to be included in the performance indices to reflect changing goals and objectives. For example, control strategies which systematically delay traffic in a network during certain periods of the day to control the volume of traffic entering a central business district or a major freeway may well be optimal from an overall system point of view. Such a strategy, which has had some preliminary evaluation in Europe (12), effectively uses the vehicle storage capacity of the network to manage traffic flow in a manner very similar to conventional ramp-metering on a motorway.

Another example where a different performance index is appropriate is the case where chronic congestion is unavoidable, and traffic must be managed to allow various competing users equal access to a particular facility, such as a motorway. Safety, which is usually considered as a constraint, could also be incorporated directly into the performance index.

With regard to motorway traffic management, future systems will continue to use conventional strategies such as ramp metering and dynamic mainline control like advisory speed and headway warning messages. The use of real-time dynamic traffic simulation programs will lead to improved on-line performance of incident detection and traffic management algorithms, and will serve as an effective tool for evaluation of new strategies before implementation.

There is, however, a limit on what can be achieved by conventional flow control. Route control is the next step, which uses re-routing strategies to produce further improvements through the more effective utilisation of spare capacity in the network (21). Current re-routing strategies are of limited effectiveness because of the nonselectivity of information given to the driver (VMS, radio), except in networks with a predominant direction, such as urban corridors or motorways (though, even in these cases, the proportion of drivers going up to the end of the corridor could be rather low). In the future, the development of two-way communications links should lead to increased use of re-routing actions by selectively informing (or even routing) drivers in accordance with their own destinations (22).

The combination of a dynamic route control and dynamic signal timing control will have the consequence that overall system stability may be an important issue in the future (11). As traffic flow surges back and forth from one route to another, there is competition between the two types of control as they tend to operate at cross-purposes. This type of problem will be of increasing concern in the development of the next generation of traffic management strategies based on the availability of new in-vehicle technology.

Road pricing and restrictive zoning strategies have so far only been applied in a few instances, and would appear to be restricted initially to closed areas where the automobile population is relatively fixed. Using the concept of what could be called 'electronic currency', these systems are highly controversial and their future application will depend on the resolution of the problem of perceived invasion of privacy and infringement on democratic freedom. There are technical means of ensuring anonymity, but the public will have to be convinced of this before accepting this type of control. Actually, automatic route guidance systems may face the same problem, but the benefits may be perceived as outweighing the potential invasion of privacy.

V.2.3. Fleet management systems

Public transit authorities were pioneers in the application of in-vehicle technology. Automatic vehicle monitoring and control systems using in-vehicle microprocessor-based radio transceivers and cellular radio systems for two-way data and voice communications were developed almost a decade ago, and are being operated successfully in a number of transit properties throughout the industrialised world. No doubt they will continue to utilise the latest technology to improve the effectiveness of their operations using new in-vehicle devices for drivers' aid, automatic fare collection (microchip card with microwave communications) and passenger information and telematics (home terminals, public terminals for computerised trip planning and automatic ticket delivery, etc.). These improvements will contribute to slowing down the growth of demand towards individual vehicle use, which will, nevertheless, remain the general trend because of its convenience, except in the case of a severe crisis.

Emergency vehicle fleets (police, fire, ambulance), and other fleets (taxis, commercial vehicles, etc.), are often already equipped with their own systems for communicating with, and dispatching, their vehicles throughout the network. It seems likely that the in-vehicle systems which are coming on the market will find application first with these special fleets, particularly those engaged in goods delivery or those providing emergency or similar services, where time is of the essence. They could, in fact, be the forerunner of in-vehicle route guidance systems for the private automobile. Developments in this area should be monitored carefully by public authorities with an eye to the possible widespread application of this technology in the future.

V.2.4. Integrated urban traffic management

During the past decade, there have been many different computerised control systems installed throughout the industrialised world to control traffic on the roadway system. As is clearly evident from Table III.1, this has included a wide variety of individual systems, including area traffic signal control systems, motorway ramp metering and speed control systems, traffic diversion and route control systems and automatic vehicle monitoring and control systems for bus transit and other fleets (23). These systems often co-exist in an urban area and yet operate independently from their own separate control centre. It is becoming increasingly clear that some degree of integration will be necessary in order to achieve maximum efficiency of the traffic system as a whole.

The degree of integration will depend on the amount of interaction or interdependence which exists between the systems. There is, for example, clearly a need for integration between a motorway traffic management system and the area traffic control system controlling the adjacent street network. An early example of this was the North Central Expressway Corridor system in Dallas, Texas (13), which co-ordinated freeway ramp metering and arterial signal control. The Glasgow CITRAC Project (14) is another example of this type of integration.

There is also a need for some degree of integration between an area traffic control system and a bus monitoring control system to give priority to buses at signalised intersections. There are some cases where this has already been done. For example, in Nancy (France), the two system computers are linked together allowing the bus system computer to ask the area traffic computer for green at any traffic signal being approached by a bus.

Ideally, it is best to plan an integrated traffic management system from the very beginning, i.e. before any systems are installed. In this way, system interfaces and the hierarchical control structure can be defined at the time each individual system is specified. This allows great flexibility in the choice and location of the control centre(s) and in the co-ordinated development of application-specific and integrated control strategies, as well as the associated software. Potential jurisdictional disputes can be resolved at the outset, and plans can be made to consolidate existing resources and staff to the highest extent possible. Cities without previous systems, or those planning to replace old systems, are in this envious position. A good example of such integrated systems is the Long Island, N.Y. motorway corridor which has been designed from the beginning on a real corridor basis and can divert traffic to adjacent signalised arterials (15).

Before the full benefits of integration can be achieved, it will be necessary to place considerably greater emphasis on the development of integrated traffic management strategies and the associated algorithms (24). This is particularly so for conventional direct traffic control systems where optimal control strategies are well established in a number of areas. There are, for example, many different programs for optimising traffic flow in signalised networks. Similarly, there are also programs for generating optimal ramp metering rates for freeways. However, there is not, as yet, a program which simultaneously optimises both, although this is an active research topic in many countries. The problem of over-saturated periods, which are frequent in Europe, is another challenge. The expert system approach and, generally speaking, the approach which tends to give aid to the operator (16), as opposed to the former "mathematical optimisation" approach, could well be a relevant alternative in the case of those big over-saturated systems which are sometimes, and to some extent, not theoretically controllable. The need for developing algorithms allowing the integration of in-vehicle route guidance systems will also appear in proportion to their future dissemination among traffic.

The ability to expand and adapt a system to new and different situations with a minimum of disruption is an important attribute. Increasingly, such flexibility will have to be built into new systems by using structured software and standardized protocols for inter-system data exchange. Perhaps a structured language should be generally used to facilitate modifications and additions to control software as well as portability between systems. The so-called "software bottleneck" could be a serious impediment to the future development of integrated traffic management systems unless a more structured, standardized approach is taken in the future.

Finally, the need for effective tools for traffic operation evaluation will become more and more apparent: off-time evaluation in order to define traffic management strategies and on-line evaluation in order to check whether some change in the traffic pattern would not justify a "re-routing" of the strategy. In this respect, the continuing development of improved traffic models and simulation programs can be anticipated, as well as new techniques like automatic vehicle monitoring (25).

All these developments will be undertaken in the future under the double pressure of the community's and the individual's interests. In view of the considerable progress of communications and high technology, people will ask for more and more efficiency in the field of road transport, and especially for individual car mobility. Public authorities in charge of broader interests, such as, for example, environmental concerns, could well adopt policies which would be perceived as good for the community and, nevertheless, harm individual car driver's interests (physical restriction of access to urban centres, urban tolls, etc.), these policies being sometimes possible thanks to this very new technological progress. It appears, therefore, that some trade-offs will have to be made to ensure some optimal operation for both the individual and the community.

REFERENCES

1. CASE, ER. Directions in urban traffic management. Conference on Transportation Engineering Practice in the 80s. Canadian Society of Civil Engineers. Toronto, April 1981.

2. TARNOFF, TJ. Artificial Intelligence and its application to traffic signal control. Transportation Research Board Conference Session on Traffic Control in the 21st Century. 64th Annual Meeting of TRB. Washington D.C., January 1985.

3. CASE, ER and WILLIAMS, KM. QEW Freeway surveillance and control system demonstration project. TRB Transportation Research Record 682. Washington D.C., 1978.

4. ISAKSEN, L and PAYNE, HJ. Freeway traffic surveillance and control. Proceedings of the IEEE. Vol. 61, No. 5. New York, May 1973.

5. PAPAGEORGIOU, M. Multilayer control system design applied to freeway traffic. IEEE Transactions on Automatic Control. Vol. AC-29, No. 6. New York, June 1984.

6. VAMOS, T. Co-operative systems based on non-co-operative people. IEEE Control Systems Magazine. New York, August 1983.

7. LESSER, VR and CORKILL, DD. Functionally accurate, co-operative distributed systems. IEEE Transactions on Systems, Man and Cybernetics. Vol. SMC-11, No. 1. New York, January 1981.

8. FORASTE, B and SCEMAMA, G. Surveillance and congested traffic control in Paris by expert systems. International Conference on Road Traffic Control, IEE. London, April 1986.

9. PAPPIS, CP and MAMDANI, EH. A fuzzy logic controller for a traffic junction. IEEE Transactions on Systems, Man and Cybernetics. Vol. SMC-7. New York, October 1977.

10. SMITH, SA and MILLER, LM. Concepts for a low cost motorist information system prepared for the U.S. Federal Highway Administration. Contract DTFH61-83-C-00059. FHWA. Washington, October 1984.

11. LUK, JYK. Direct traffic control. Discussion Paper prepared for OECD Scientific Expert Group MC3. Australian Road Research Board. Vermont South, 1985.

12. FARGIER, PH et al. Reducing travel time by freeway ramp metering especially when peak traffic demand exceeds corridor capacity. International Symposium on Traffic Control Systems. Berkeley, August 1979.

13. CARVELL, Jr, JD. Dallas corridor study: final report. Federal Highway Administration, FHWA-RG-77-15. Washington, March 1976.

14. MOWATT, AM and YOUNG, AD. CITRAC — the first five years. Traffic Engineering and Control. London, May 1984.

15. ZOVE, P. and BERGER, C. Integrated motorist information system (IMIS) feasibility and design study, phase I: feasibility study. Report No. FHWA-RD-77-49. U.S. Federal Highway Administration, Washington, April 1977.

16. MORIN, JM and PIERRELEE, JC. SIRTAKI, an aid to real-time decision making for motorway access control. PTRC. Brighton, July 1986.

17. HAUTALA, P and NYSTEN, E. Weather detection and prediction within the Euco-cost 30 bis project. International Seminar CEC/ECMT/COST on Electronics and Traffic on Major Roads. OECD, Paris, 1985.

18. BLOSSEVILLE, JM. Stratégie adaptative de contrôle d'un accès à une autoroute. INRETS. Paris, 1985.

19. MARTIN, JA. Automatic incident detection, report from Cost 30 bis — working group 2. International Seminar CEC/ECMT/COST on Electronics and Traffic on Major Roads. OECD, Paris, 1985.

20. LESORT, JB. Régulation centralisée de la circulation en ville. Rapport de recherche n° 17. INRETS. Paris, 1984.

21. DESFORGES, O, LA BRETEQUE, DE, L, COTTINET, M and LESORT, JB. Gestion dynamique d'itinéraires urbains. INRETS. Paris, 1982.

22. RUENAUFER, P et al. Technologien für integrierte Strassenverkehrsleit-systeme. Richtstudien. Bundesministerium für Forschung und Technologie. Bonn, 1982.

23. STEIERWALD, G and ZACKOR, H. Requirements for an integrated traffic control system on major roads including individual communication. International Seminar CEC/ECMT/COST on Electronics and Traffic on Major Roads. OECD, Paris, 1985.

24. LUK, JYK. Tests on a heuristic algorithm for a combined area traffic control — assignment problem. Vol. 9, Part 5. ARRB proceedings. Vermont South (Victoria), 1978.

25. LUK, JYK. Vehicle identification and the evaluation of area traffic control systems. ARRB. Vermont South (Victoria), 1983.

Chapter VI

CONCLUSIONS AND RECOMMENDATIONS

While the foregoing sections of the report have described the general background of dynamic traffic management systems and forecasted the likely trends in this field, this Chapter puts forward the Group's conclusions and recommendations in the three sections of driver information, direct traffic control, and public transport and fleet control.

VI.1. DRIVER INFORMATION

VI.1.1. Conclusions

There is a continuous need for better road information. This is often expressed by drivers and has been recognised by traffic authorities. Important benefits are anticipated for individuals and the community through improvements in this field; these concern reductions in traffic congestion, energy consumption and environmental effects, travel time, maintenance and safety costs. According to a recent EUCO COST 30 estimation, a European route guidance and hazard warning system could save approximately ECU 2 400 million (1984) per year in urban and rural areas.

Progress in information technologies offers new opportunities for improved road information delivery focusing on trip planning (teletext, videotex, cable T.V.) and en-route information and navigation aids (variable message signs, in-vehicle devices, etc.). Some new systems are already being made available to the public, while others are very close to the production stage.

To some extent, it is difficult from the various surveys which have been conducted, to predict the likely market penetration of these new devices. However, it is well known that new devices often create new needs because of the new capacities they can offer, and these needs help in their dissemination among users. This could well be the case in the field of driver information, provided drivers can be given better information (together with other services) at a reasonable cost. After the first stage, when the initial costs involved will restrict the use to professional or luxury vehicles, in-vehicle equipment will become cheaper thanks to manufacturers' competition and technological progress.

Conventional information systems (media, telephone, special traffic information broadcasting, citizens band radio, variable message signs) will probably still be in use for decades and give very valuable results, especially through the improvements which will be made (for example, the digitalization of special traffic broadcasting services). In this respect, national radio traffic information, which is commonly used, has a low efficiency (addressing unconcerned drivers, experiencing great delays, etc.). Attempts are being made to use local radio braodcasting, especially on motorways. These systems are felt to provide a valuable alternative until more selective and efficient systems are implemented (digital information broadcasting, for example), but they are faced with legal and capacity restrictions (lack of available frequencies) in many countries.

Both for conventional and new systems, data gathering and processing (collation and consolidation) is a major issue. It now appears that this is the weak link in the road information chain: important delays are often noticed between an accident's occurence and the time it is reported to motorists, which hampers driver trust in the system.

Both when collecting and disseminating data, a general problem of organisation often exists. Public and private organisations (broadcasting companies, automobile associations, etc.) sometimes work in the same area with little co-operation, although they could assist each other. Also, among public administrations, problems of jurisdiction sometimes occur; for example, the police's first concern is generally safety, and the collection of traffic information and its transmission to management authorities are often second priority.

In-vehicle information (whether it concerns traffic or the vehicle's operation) raises some ergonomic problems which have been studied by institutes and car manufacturers in several countries. This information could interfere with the driving task and some negative effects on safety could be anticipated. Solutions like head-up display (used in aeronautics), vocal recall of visual information and inhibition of some functions while moving are being investigated.

Overall, in the field of information, the problem of driver acceptance is of crucial importance. Common experience has shown that information systems have often been denigrated by drivers because they gave bad information. This phenomenon is particularly strong in circumstances when drivers are diverted from their intended travel pattern without any reason.

VI.1.2. Recommendations

The rapid progress in information technologies should be utilised in the field of road information where important benefits are at stake for society and the driver (time savings, safety, energy consumption, air and noise pollution, comfort) and where important industrial implications (automobile market) exist.

In order to ensure compatibility of different in-vehicle equipment across borders, a standardization effort is recommended in the field of data dissemination protocols: ideally one single interface should be agreed upon for road-to-vehicle communications.

Some standardization of in-vehicle information language should also occur as has already been done, for example, in Europe for external road and information signs. Vehicle-borne route guidance systems also need standards for the digital mapping of road networks.

Concerning in-vehicle information, the choice of digital data dissemination techniques is strongly recommended. These techniques make it possible, by means of special codings, to address the types of vehicles to be informed. The driver also has the option of selecting the type of information he receives. Moreover, it makes it possible to receive the same message in several languages (voice synthesis or literary messages) and to display pictograms, which are essential for transnational trips. For example, concerning Europe, the EUCO-COST 30 bis co-operation group on road/vehicle electronic communication strongly supported the creation of a common dedicated digital data radio broadcasting channel allowing:

-- Updates of vehicle-borne route guidance systems; and
-- Selective dissemination of road information to all vehicles provided they are equipped with the minimum information receiver unit.

In this respect, the envisaged pan-European cellular radio telephone broadcasting network could be a good opportunity allowing, moreover, connection with videotex services. However, other alternatives exist, such as roadside beacons, in-vehicle teletext.

As regards trip planning, the spreading of telematics (teletext, videotex) offers increasing potential. Such techniques should be used extensively to aid motorists, whether at home before starting or en route at special locations (rest areas, fuel stations, etc.).

The improvement of traffic data collection is the first priority task to be undertaken, i.e. the improvement of current technologies as well as development of new technologies which could give way to new traffic description parameters. Important gains are also foreseeable through the rationalization of data collection organisations. In this respect, improved co-operation between public and private agencies is recommended.

All these improvements will be beneficial to both conventional and new information means. They are, in some manner, imposed by the progress of communication technologies, which is led by industry. This is a challenge for public authorities who are in charge of general traffic management.

Ergonomic aspects should be carefully investigated to detect the possible negative effects of in-vehicle information on safety (overload of the driving task). A global approach, integrating information means and other driving aids (autonomous active safety equipment, like radar, or automatic alarms to warn non-vigilant drivers), should be adopted.

Public acceptance is a major issue in the field of driver information. It is strongly recommended that before putting new systems into action, careful investigations be conducted so as to ensure that they are properly used.

VI.2. DIRECT TRAFFIC CONTROL

VI.2.1. Conclusions

Dynamic traffic management systems are under development in most industrialised countries: centralised urban traffic control, traffic-responsive ramp metering and dynamic speed control in motorway systems, traffic re-routing using variable message signs, etc.

Tools are being developed and improved for the definition and operation of real-time traffic signal control strategies. However, this sort of control will soon reach its maximum efficiency. Re-routing strategies are the next step which should allow further improvements through the use of temporarily free network capacity (in case of an incident, for example). Due to the lack of selectivity of current information systems, re-routing is only effective when there exists a preferential direction in the network (a "corridor"). Future development of automatic route guidance should nevertheless increase its effectiveness because it will allow the selective routing of drivers through the network in accordance with their destinations.

Increasing attention is being paid to the feed-back effects of traffic control on demand through induced changes in routes or departure times. This will become an even more important issue in view of the future use of route control and the consequent stability problems. Co-ordination between route control and traffic signal control is therefore necessary.

Integration problems exist for both co-ordinating strategies used in inter-related systems (area control and motorway control, for example) and co-ordinating the various traffic management bodies involved.

Conventional control tools such as area-wide traffic control, ramp metering and variable message signs (advisory speed, lane allocation, headway warning, etc.) will remain in use for decades. They will profit by the progress in technology, which will further improve their efficiency (for example, the use of light emitting diodes for variable message signs, etc.).

As in the field of driver information, there is a need for good traffic data collection giving a better description of actual traffic patterns and short-term forecasts. Models which could give a reasonably good estimation of traffic patterns by using a limited, but well-chosen, number of sensors would be of great interest.

With regard to the increasing complexity of traffic control in large urban and suburban road systems, and to the difficulty of defining "optimal" strategies, there is a clear need for developing aids for system operators.

A general need for the elaboration of methodologies and tools for a priori and a posteriori evaluation of traffic control strategies exists, in order to assess their efficiency and detect needed changes in time.

VI.2.2. Recommendations

Research should continue in the field of traffic modelling and forecasting, definition of control strategies and the development of aids for systems operators. New techniques like real-time traffic simulation, enabling the use of optimal control, and artificial intelligence (knowledge-based systems) are promising and should be investigated.

Organisational problems must be solved for improved co-ordination of control strategies and improved data collection.

The development of new technologies (sensors, processors) should be monitored for possible application in the field of traffic management with a view to enhancing existing means and developing new parameters for traffic description (automatic collection of origin-destination data, travel time or trip data, queue lengths, turning movements, etc.) and the corresponding new control algorithms.

Control tools like electronic road pricing should be carefully evaluated before implementation in particular in regard to problems of public acceptance and privacy. However, since it is likely that restrictions of access to town centres will have to be carefully considered in the future, it is recommended to progress toward the development of electronic road pricing systems which do not require driver identification.

New concepts are now conceivable due to the tremendous development of microelectronics, image processing and artificial intelligence (automatically driven vehicle, automatic flow, electronic vehicle detection, in-vehicle green wave, etc.) and could be at hand within twenty to thirty years. These should represent a revolution for traffic management. Since these developments in in-vehicle equipment would have important effects on traffic, it is recommended that public authorities responsible for traffic management be involved to ensure they will fit with the global traffic scenario which will be considered desirable in the future.

In view of the time lapse before these new control tools and concepts are implemented, efforts to enhance conventional control tools should actively continue. New hardware and software techniques are believed to provide promising applications and should be tested in the field of traffic management. For example, automatic video image processing used to detect turning movements at intersections could give way to great improvements in area-wide traffic control, just as expert systems could for large saturated networks.

Evaluation tools (using techniques like statistical experimental design, simulation, etc.) should be further developed to give more accurate assessments of the efficiency of traffic control strategies.

VI.3. PUBLIC TRANSPORT AND FLEET CONTROL

VI.3.1. Conclusions

Public transport is part of whole transport system. Competition between public transport and individual car traffic exists because both are sharing the same infrastructure. Therefore there is a clear need for integration.

Public transport has a direct social utility. It provides people who do not have an individual car, or who do not want to use it, with travel facility. This is why its operation must be protected against the demands of individual car traffic. Moreover, it is probably more consistent with the optimisation of the global transport system.

Efforts have been made and are continuing for the promotion of public transport (bus lane allocation, centralised control, etc.). But this policy has contributed more to safeguard the quality of service than to induce a modal shift from the individual car to public transport. This promotion remains all the more necessary as car traffic is continuing to increase. If this trend proves to be stable, the use of individual cars in town centres will probably have to be restricted, thereby contributing to the development of public transport, in conventional or new forms.

Concerning special fleets (police, fire-brigades, ambulance, taxis, goods delivery vehicles), many of them are already equipped with communication means to their own control centres, which can locate them and manage their trips. Automatic systems exist which could presage the future private car information and guidance systems. The integration of these special fleet control systems into the global traffic management system is an important issue, especially for emergency vehicles (priority treatment) and for the global management operation ("in-the-flow" data collection). Moreover, special fleets constitute a useful experimental vehicle park for testing first generation in-vehicle navigation and guidance equipment before its dissemination to the public.

VI.3.2.   Recommendations

Integration of private car traffic, public transport and special fleets should be pursued, especially by providing links between different control centres. As mentioned in several places in this report, this could raise problems of co-ordination between different public and private bodies which should be addressed.

Promotion of public transport should continue using the development of in-vehicle electronic devices (driver aids and passenger information), electronic currency (credit cards, smart cards), and telematics (home terminals, public information terminals for computerised trip planning and automatic ticket delivery, etc.) engendered by the enormous progress of current electronic technology (bubble and laser video disk memories, chip cards, etc.).

Political choices concerning the balance between private car use and public transport should be considered in advance, to best prepare the urban travel conditions of the end of the century.

ANNEX 1

This Annex gives a list of references for each class of existing systems for which documentation was available.

Class 1: Media

Class 2: Telephone Pre-trip Information Services

CENTRE REGIONAL D'INFORMATION ET DE COORDINATION ROUTIERES d'Ile de France. Ministères de la Défense, de l'Intérieur et des Transports. Paris, November 1984.

Class 3: Teletext Pre-trip Information Services

ANTIOPE-ROUTE: pour mieux vivre la route, des pages d'informations actualisées en permanence. Direction de la Sécurité et de la Circulation Routières. Paris.

Class 4: Videotex Route Planning Services

ROUTE-TEL, a viewdata route planning service for drivers. Leaflet 952. TRRL. Crowthorne, Feb. 1983.

PAQUET, C. Les applications du Vidéotex à la Direction de la Sécurité et de la Circulation Routière. 1982.

Class 5: Special Traffic Information Broadcasting Services

TURNAGE, HC. Highway Advisory Radio. Vol. VT-29, No.2. IEEE Transactions on vehicular technology. May 1980.

MAMMANO, FJ. Speech synthesis for a motorist information system -- AHAR System. OECD seminar on micro-electronics for road and traffic management. Traffic Bureau Police National Agency. Tokyo 1985.

Class 6: Citizen's Band Radio

Class 7: Vehicle Borne Route Guidance Aids with Radio Broadcast Updating

Mobile information systems project. Traffic Engineering and Control. July/August 1984.

KOSHI, Masaki. Some aspects of land vehicle navigation in Japan. University of Tokyo.

PILSAK, O. EVA, an Electronic traffic pilot for motorists. Symposium on land vehicle navigation. Deutsche Gesellschaft für Ortung un Navigation EV. Münster, 1984.

COTTINET, M. DANA, un dispositif d'aide à la navigation des automobilistes. Institut national de recherche sur les transports et leur sécurité (INRETS). Paris, 1985.

91

Class 7: <u>Vehicle Borne Route Guidance Aids with Radio Broadcast Updating</u>
(Cont'd)

HENRY, JJ.   Etude des systèmes de localisation et de guidage des véhicules.   ONERA/CERT.   Jan. 1982.

HAEUSSERMANN, P.   On-board computer system for navigation, orientation and route optimisation.   ROUTEN-TECHNER.   Society of automotive engineers, International congress and exposition.   Detroit, March 1984.

Class 8: <u>Variable Message Sign and Route Control Systems</u>

A new motorway signal.   Traffic engineering and control.   November 1983.

Automatic speed warning signs.   Report LR 1118.   TRRL.   Crowthorne, Nov. 1984.

Keiyo area traffic information provision system.   Japan highway public corporation.

DUDEK et al.   Manual on real-time motorist information displays.   FHWA.   Washington, May 1984.

DUDEK, CL et al.   Real-time freeway-to-freeway diversion: the San Antonio experience.   Transportation research record 841.   1982.

TSUZAWA, M and MOCHIZUKI, M.   Variable information board employing LED and solar battery.   OECD Seminar on Micro-electronics for Road and Traffic Management.   Traffic Bureau National Police Agency.   Tokyo, 1984.

Panneaux variables d'information routière en milieu urbain.   Ingénieurs des villes de France.   1983.

WECKESSER, PM and KRAFT, J.   New Jersey turnpike automatic traffic surveillance and control system performance observation.   Transport Research Board record 816.   TRB.   Washington, 1981.

BEUKERS, B.   The Dutch motorway control and signalling system and its effects on road safety and traffic flow.   OECD Seminar on Micro-electronics for Road and Traffic Management.   Traffic Bureau National Police Agency.   Tokyo, 1984.

BOLTE, F et al.   Die Stauwarnanlage tichelberg.   Strasse und Autobahn 28.   Heft 7.   1977.

PIERRE-BLOCH, JP.   Présentation du système d'information des usagers du corridor périphérique par panneaux et messages variables.   Mairie de Paris, May 1985.

ANDREWS, R and HILLEN, SM.   Car park variable message signs in Torbay, Devon.   PTRC annual summer meeting.   July 1980.

Class 9: Historic Urban Traffic Control, Tidal Flow, and Ramp Metering Systems
and
Class 10: Adaptive Urban Traffic Control, Tidal Flow and Ramp Metering Systems

LUK, JYK. Two traffic-responsive area traffic control methods: SCAT and SCOOT. Traffic engineering and control. Jan. 1984.

MOWATT, AM and YOUNG, AD. CITRAC, the first five years. Traffic engineering and control. May 1984.

LESORT, JB. The ZELT operation: a site for traffic control experiments. Traffic engineering and control. April 1985.

LONGFOOT, JE. Control system for three lane Tidal Flow Bridges. Vol. 12, Part 5. ARRB proceedings. 1984.

Integrated motorist information system (IMIS). Phase III: Development of detailed design and plans, specifications and estimates. Report RD-82/108. FHWA. Washington, Oct. 1982.

RICHARDSON, DB. Metropolitan Toronto's new system. Engineering foundation conference on traffic monitoring and control systems. Henmiker, New Hampshire, June 1983.

LOWRIE, PR. The Sydney co-ordinated adaptive traffic system (SCATS) -- principles, methodology, algorithms. International conference on road traffic signalling. IEE. London, 1982.

HOFFMANN, A et al. Überarbeitung und Buvertung der Signalsteuerung des Stadt Hamburg. Strassenverkehrstechnik. Heft 5. 1984.

HUNT, PB et al. SCOOT -- a traffic responsive method of co-ordinating signals. Report 1014. TRRL. Crowthorne, 1981.

CASE, ER and WILLIAMS, KM. Queen Elizabeth way freeway surveillance and control system demonstration project. Transportation research record 682. 1978.

La régulation des feux de signalisation à Paris. Mairie de Paris. Octobre 1983.

MORIN, JM and PIERRELEE, JC. SIRTAKI, an aid to real-time decision-making for motorway access control. 14th summer annual meeting. PTRC. Brighton. 1986.

SUZUKI, M. Area traffic control systems in Japan. OECD Seminar on Micro-electronics for Road and Traffic Management. Traffic Bureau National Police Agency. Tokyo, 1984.

HARMELINK, MD et al. Freeway traffic management on highway 401, Toronto, Canada. TRR. 1982.

The Hanshin express way traffic control system. Computer controlled urban transportation in international series on applied systems analysis No. 10. IIASA. 1982.

Class 11: Automatic Route Guidance Systems

A universal traffic guidance and information system. Symposium on land vehicle navigation. Deutsche Gesellschaft für Ortung un Navigation EV. Münster, 1984.

ROSEN, DA et al. An electronic route-guidance system (ERGS) for highway vehicles. IEEE Transactions on vehicular technology. Volume VT-19 No. 1. 1970.

Felderprobung lines Zielführungus-und Informationssystems für Autofahrer(ALI). Bundes Ministerium für Forschung un Technologie (BMFT). 1978.

ONDA, M. Comprehensive automobile control system (CACS). Research association for comprehensive automobile control technology. MITI. Japan, 1976.

BUO, N et al. Outline of the CASC pilot test system. Proceedings of the 58th annual meeting. Transportation Research Board. Washington DC, 1979.

Zielführungs-und Informationssystem ALI; Fryebnisse der Felderprobung. Technischer Überwachungs-Verein Rheinland. Cologne, 1981.

TOMKEWITSCH, VAN, R. Communication between information beacons and vehicles provided with infrared equipment. AUTO-SCOOT. OECD Seminar on Micro-electronics for Road and Traffic Management. Traffic Bureau National Police Agency. Tokyo, 1984.

SVIDEN O. ARISE, automobile road information system evolution. 14th annual summer meeting. PTRC. Brighton, 1986.

Class 12: Road Pricing and Automatic Vehicle Location Systems

DAWSON, AL. Electronic road pricing in Hong-Kong: the pilot stage. Traffic engineering and control. August 1983.

Electronic road pricing in Hong-Kong: 1. DAWSON, AL and BROWN, FN. A fair way to go? 2. CATLING, I and HARBORD, BJ. The technology. 3. HARRISON, B. Estimating and evaluating the effects. Traffic engineering and control. Nov-Dec 1985, Jan. 1986.

Class 13: Signal Priority Systems

BOSSERHOFF, D and SWIDERSKI, D. Priority for emergency vehicles by intervention in signal-setting programs. Traffic engineering and control. June 1984.

PHILIPPS, P. Public transport priority at traffic lights by linkage of traffic control system and public transport control system. International conference on road traffic signalling. IEE. London, 1982.

Class 13: <u>Signal Priority Systems</u> (Cont'd)

HUBSCHNEIDER, H. and MOTT, PE. Bus priority using a bus guidance and control system -- a simulation study. International conference in road traffic signalling. IEE. London, 1982.

CORNWELL, PR. et al. Tram priority in SCATS. Traffic engineering and control. November, 1986.

Class 14: <u>Vehicle Fleet Command and Control Systems</u>

Computerised traffic control for taxis in Norway's capital. Traffic engineering and control. November, 1983.

Guide 85 des systèmes automatiques d'information. Centre d'études des transports urbains. Paris, 1985.

Systèmes d'aide à l'exploitation des transports publics urbains. Centre d'études des transports urbains. Paris, 1983.

FELZ, H. Standardisiertes rechnesgesteuertes Betriebsleitsystem für den offentlichen Nahverkehr. Verkehr und Technik. Heft 9. 1981.

ANNEX 2

LIST OF OECD STUDIES ON TRAFFIC MANAGEMENT
AND CONTROL SYSTEMS AND STRATEGIES

2.1 OECD Publications

-- Electronic aids for freeway operations. Chairman: Dr. K. Krell, Germany. 1971.

-- Area traffic control systems. Chairman: Mr. J.H. Hillier, United Kingdom. 1972.

-- Research on traffic corridor control. Chairman: Dr. W.W. Wolman, United States. 1975.

-- Integrated urban traffic management. Chairman: Dr. W.W. Wolman, United States. 1978.

-- Traffic measurement methods for urban and suburban areas. Chairman: Mr. S.K. Nielsen, Denmark. 1979.

-- Traffic control in saturated conditions. Chairman: Mr. J.J. Klijnhout, The Netherlands. 1981.

-- Automobile fuel consumption in actual traffic conditions. Chairman: Mr. C. Lamure, France. 1982.

-- Assessing fuel savings through traffic management. Chairman: Professor Koshi, Japan. 1984.

2.2 Seminars and Symposia

-- Traffic control and driver communication*. Seminar held in Aachen and organised by Germany. 1982.

_____

* Proceedings available in the host country.

-- <u>Micro-electronics for road and traffic management</u>*. Seminar held in Tokyo and organised by Japan. 1984.

2.3 <u>On-going activity</u>

-- <u>Driver information and guidance systems using in-car communication</u>. Chairman: Dr. Bolte, Germany.

---

*   Proceedings available in the host country.

LIST OF MEMBERS OF THE GROUP

Chairman: Mr. J.M. MORIN (France)

Australia
Mr. J. LUK (Corresponding Member)
Australian Road Research Board
PO Box 156 (Bag 4)
Nunawading, Victoria 3131

Belgium
Mr. C. LEJEUNE
Inspecteur général des Ponts et Chaussées
Administration des Routes
Ministère des Travaux Publics
Avenue Simon Bolivar 30
B-1210 Bruxelles

Mr. P. TIELEMANS
Ingénieur en Chef -- Directeur des Ponts et Chaussées
Administration des Routes
Ministère des Travaux Publics
Avenue Simon Bolivar 30
B-1210 Bruxelles

Canada
Mr. E.R. CASE, P.Eng.
Principal Research Engineer
Research and Development Branch
Ontario Ministry of Transportation and Communications
1201 Wilson Avenue
Downsview, Ontario M3M 1J8

France
Mr. M. BOUSSUGE
DTCS/SETRA
46 avenue Aristide Briand
BP 100
92223 Bagneux

Mr. J.M. MORIN (Chairman)
Institut National de Recherche sur les Transports
  et leur Sécurité (INRETS)
2 avenue du Général Malleret-Joinville
94114 Arcueil Cedex

Germany
Dr. P. RÜENAUFER
TUV Rheinland
Stabsstelle Projektbegleitung
Postfach 10 17 50
5000 Cologne 1

Italy   Dr.Ing. F. TREGLIA
                         Autostrade S.p.A.
                         Via Bergamini 50
                         00159 Roma

                         Mr. V. DI TOMASO
                         Autostrade S.p.A.
                         Via Bergamini 50
                         00159 Roma

Japan   Mr. M. KATAKURA
                         Assistant Professor
                         Institute of Industrial Science
                         Tokyo University
                         7-22-1 Roppongi, Minato-ku
                         Tokyo

Netherlands   Mr. H. REMEIJN
                         Transport and Traffic Engineering Division
                         Rijkswaterstaat
                         PO Box 20906
                         2500 EX The Hague

United Kingdom   Mr. D. JEFFERY
                         Transport and Road Research Laboratory
                         Old Wokingham Road
                         Crowthorne
                         Berks, HG11 6AU

United States   Mr. D.A. ROSEN
                         Highway Research Engineer
                         Urban Traffic Management Division (HSR-40)
                         Federal Highway Administration
                         Department of Transportation
                         6300 Georgetown Pike
                         McLean, Virginia 22101

OECD   Mr. B. HORN
                         Mr. C. MORIN

The rapporteurs for the various chapters were:
Mr. J.M. Morin (Chairman), Mr. M. Boussuge, Mr. E.R. Case,
Mr. D. Jeffery, Mr. C. Lejeune, Mr. H. Remeijn, Dr. P. Rüenaufer and
Mr. C. Morin (OECD).

Also available

OECD ROAD TRANSPORT RESEARCH PROGRAMME

ENERGY SAVINGS AND ROAD TRAFFIC MANAGEMENT. Report prepared by an OECD Scientific Expert Group (September 1985)
(77 85 02 1) ISBN 92-64-12753-4   114 pages £8.20   US$16.00   F82.00   DM36.00

TRAFFIC CAPACITY OF MAJOR ROUTES. Report prepared by an OECD Scientific Expert Group, July 1983 (October 1983)
(77 83 03 1) ISBN 92-64-12480-2   120 pages £6.50   US$13.00   F65.00   DM29.00

AUTOMOBILE FUEL CONSUMPTION IN ACTUAL TRAFFIC CONDITIONS. Report prepared by an OECD Road Research Group, December 1981 (April 1982)
(77 82 01 1) ISBN 92-64-12304-0   118 pages £3.80   US$8.50   F38.00   DM19.00

TRAFFIC CONTROL IN SATURATED CONDITIONS (January 1981)
(77 81 02 1) ISBN 92-64-12154-4   86 pages £3.60   US$9.00   F36.00   DM18.00

EVALUATION OF URBAN PARKING SYSTEMS (December 1980)
(77 80 05 1) ISBN 92-64-12139-0   108 pages £4.00   US$10.00   F40.00   DM20.00

Prices charged at the OECD Bookshop.

*THE OECD CATALOGUE OF PUBLICATIONS and supplements will be sent free of charge
on request addressed either to OECD Publications Service, Sales and Distribution Division,
2, rue André-Pascal, 75775 PARIS CEDEX 16, or to the OECD Sales Agent in your country.*

OECD PUBLICATIONS, 2, rue André-Pascal, 75775 PARIS CEDEX 16 - No. 43955 1987
PRINTED IN FRANCE
(77 87 02 1) ISBN 92-64-12926-X